MW00561023

THE LANGUAGE GYM

FRENCH SENTENCE BUILDERS

A lexicogrammar approach

PRIMARY

PART 2

THE LANGUAGE GYM

Copyright © G. Conti and D. Viñales

All rights reserved

ISBN: 9783949651663

This book is fully photocopiable but may not be scanned and shared

Imprint: Language Gym

THE LANGUAGE GYM

DEDICATION

For my daughter Giulia

-Simona

For my family & Deirdre Jones

-Stefano

For Catrina

-Gianfranco

For Ariella & Leonard

-Dylan

For Horatio

-Aurélie

For Inaya

-Nadim

For Luc

-Jérôme

About the authors

Simona Gravina has taught for 16 years, in schools in Italy and the UK, both in state and independent settings. She lives in Glasgow, Scotland. She is fluent in three languages and gets by in a few more. Simona is, besides a teacher, a mum, a bookworm, a passionate traveller and a fitness enthusiast. In the last couple of years she has been testing and implementing E.P.I. in one of the top Independent schools in Scotland, St Aloysius' College, where she is currently Modern Languages Curriculum Leader in the Junior School. In addition, Simona is a committee member of SALT, Scottish Association for Languages Teachers.

Stefano Pianigiani is currently teaching languages at Temple Moor High School in Leeds, England. He teaches Spanish, Italian and French being fluent in four languages and he is also learning others. In addition he is an educator at Nuestra Escuela Leeds, the first supplementary Spanish school in Yorkshire. Stefano is a fervent creator of resources whose greatest passions are cooking and DIY. He has a wide cultural experience having studied and lived in Italy, Spain and England. He has recently completed his MA in Education at Leeds Trinity University reinforcing his knowledge and competence on how to arouse engagement adopting the communicative approach within the classroom. He is an enthusiastic educator who has fully embraced Dr Conti's teaching from its origins. His academic interest has led him to becoming a governor at St. Nicholas Catholic Primary School.

Gianfranco Conti taught for 25 years at schools in Italy, the UK and in Kuala Lumpur, Malaysia. He has also been a university lecturer, holds a Master's degree in Applied Linguistics and a PhD in metacognitive strategies as applied to second language writing. He is now an author, a popular independent educational consultant and a professional development provider. He has written around 2,000 resources for the TES website, which have awarded him the Best Resources Contributor in 2015. He has co-authored the best-selling and influential book for world languages teachers, "The Language Teacher Toolkit", "Breaking the sound barrier: Teaching learners how to listen", in which he puts forth his Listening As Modelling methodology and "Memory: what every language teacher should know". Last but not least, Gianfranco has created the instructional approach known as E.P.I. (Extensive Processing Instruction).

Dylan Viñales has taught for 16 years, in schools in Bath, Beijing and Kuala Lumpur in state, independent and international settings. He lives in Kuala Lumpur. He is fluent in five languages and gets by in several more. Dylan is, besides a teacher, a professional development provider, specialising in E.P.I., metacognition, teaching languages through music (especially ukulele) and cognitive science. In the last five years, together with Dr Conti, he has driven the implementation of E.P.I. in one of the top international schools in the world: Garden International School. Dylan authors an influential blog on modern language pedagogy in which he supports the teaching of languages through E.P.I.

About the authors

Nadim Cham has taught for the last five years in England and internationally, both in state and independent schools. He has been teaching for the last two years in Cairo, in a British International School, in which he has obtained outstanding results with his students at iGCSE level using EPI. He thoroughly enjoys collaborating with other practitioners as well as creating and sharing resources which apply the EPI pedagogy developed in this book. Nadim enjoys sports, discovering new technology, international food, and spending time with his family, as well collaborating on fantastic projects such as this book and many others, which contribute to improving the way languages are taught around the world.

Jérôme Nogues has taught for over 20 years in London and in Shropshire and state and independent schools. He is an EPI enthusiast, Head of Languages and Digital Learning in a small Prep school near Shrewsbury. He has a passion for education technology and its use in and out of the classroom to enhance teaching and learning. He regularly leads CPD sessions for fellow teachers to develop their IT skills face to face or online. When he is not busy working on wonderful projects like this one with amazing people, he enjoys spending time with his family and hitting the road or the trail to chill.

Aurélie Lethuilier has taught for 23 years and has been at her current school for 21 years (17 years as Curriculum Leader for Modern Languages). She is very passionate about teaching and learning and loves creating resources that will get the best out of students. She has been using and testing the EPI approach for a few years now and has successfully implemented it amongst her dedicated team of amazing teachers, without whom this journey would not have been possible. Within the Language Gym team, Aurélie is best known for her generosity of spirit, always going the extra mile, and for her upbeat and positive nature, all of which make her a highly valued member of the group.

Acknowledgements

Firstly, we would like to thank Simona Gravina and Stefano Pianigiani for their creation of the original Spanish Primary Sentence Book, parts 1 and 2. We believe that their passion for the teaching of languages, both at primary and secondary level, has brought the MFL community together and proven that anyone can begin to learn a foreign language, from a very young age. Their hard work has made the adaptation of this book into French a fascinating, rewarding and exciting opportunity for us.

Secondly, we would like to thank Lou Smith for her contributions during the making of this book. Her insightful suggestions in the review stage of the sentence builders and her assistance during the proofreading phase were both highly valuable in the creation and adaption of this project. We are grateful to Lou for sharing her experience and expertise with the team.

We would also like to thank Martin Lapworth for his hard work in creating a digital version of these sentence builders on **www.sentencebuilders.com**. His attention to detail, feedback, as well as his linguistic and technical skills have made him a great asset to the team.

Our sincere gratitude to all the people involved in the recording of the Listening audio files:

Lorène Martine Carver, Joanna Asse-Drouet, Nicolas Asse-Drouet, Steeve De Palmas Duflots & Isabelle Henderson. Your energy, enthusiasm and passion come across clearly in every recording and is the reason why the listening sections are such a successful and engaging resource, according to the many students who have been alpha and beta testing the book.

Thanks to **Flaticon.com** for providing access to a limitless library of engaging icons, clipart and images which we have used to make this book more user-friendly and visually appealing, with a view to be as engaging as possible for primary level students.

Finally, our gratitude to the MFL Twitterati for their ongoing support of E.P.I. and the Sentence Builders book series. In particular a shoutout to our team of incredible educators who helped in checking all the units: Lou Smith, Chris Pye, Simona Gravina, Lorène Martine Carver, Joanna Asse-Drouet, Karine Longman, Darren Lester. It is thanks to your time, patience, professionalism and detailed feedback that we have been able to produce such a refined and highly accurate product.

Merci à tous,

Jérôme, Nadim, Aurélie, Gianfranco & Dylan

 **THE LANGUAGE GYM**

Introduction

Hello and welcome to our second Sentence Builders workbook designed for Primary aged children, designed to be an accompaniment to a French Extensive Processing Instruction course. The book has come about out of necessity, because such a resource did not previously exist.

How to use this book if you have bought into our E.P.I. approach

This book was originally designed as a resource to use in conjunction with our E.P.I. approach and teaching strategies. Our course favours flooding comprehensible input, organising content by communicative functions and related constructions, and a big focus on reading and listening as modelling. The aim of this book is to empower the beginner learner with linguistic tools - high-frequency structures and vocabulary - useful for real-life communication. Since, in a typical E.P.I. unit of work, aural and oral work play a huge role, this book should not be viewed as the ultimate E.P.I. coursebook, but rather as a **useful resource** to **complement** your Listening-As-Modelling and Speaking activities.

Sentence Builders – Online Versions

Please note that all these sentence builders will be available in bilingual and French only versions on the **Language-Gym.com** website, available to download, editable and in landscape design optimised for displaying in the classroom, via the ***Locker Room** section. In addition, all the sentence builders in this book are also available on the **SentenceBuilders.com** website, together with an extensive range of self-marking homework or class assignments, designed to practice listening, reading and writing in keeping with the EPI approach (available via subscription).

*Please note that the Locker Room is only accessible via a paid subscription, as part of a full Language Gym Licence.

How to use this book if you don't know or have NOT bought into our approach

Alternatively, you may use this book to dip in and out of as a source of printable material for your lessons. Whilst our curriculum is driven by communicative functions rather than topics, we have deliberately embedded the target constructions in topics which are popular with teachers and commonly found in published coursebooks.

If you would like to learn about E.P.I. you could read one of the authors' blogs. The definitive guide is Dr Conti's "Patterns First – How I Teach Lexicogrammar" which can be found on his blog (www.gianfrancoconti.com). There are also blogs on Dylan's wordpress site (mrvinalesmfl.wordpress.com) such as "Using sentence builders to reduce (everyone's) workload and create more fluent linguists" which can be read to get teaching ideas and to learn how to structure a course, through all the stages of E.P.I.

Examples of E.P.I. activities and games to play in class, based on MARS EARS sequence, can be found in Simona's padlet (https://en-gb.padlet.com/simograv/svi55fluxeolisi9) "MFL Teaching based on E.P.I. approach, Videos and blogs, Sample activities from Modelling to Spontaneity". These can be used to model tasks.

The book "Breaking the Sound Barrier: Teaching Learners how to Listen" by Gianfranco Conti and Steve Smith, provides a detailed description of the approach and of the listening and speaking activities you can use in synergy with the present book.

 THE LANGUAGE GYM

The structure of the book

This book contains 7 units which concern themselves with different topics as listed in the Table of Contents. Each unit includes:

- a sentence builder modelling the target constructions, introduced by questions to guide communication;
- a set of Listening-As-Modelling activities to train decoding skills, sound awareness, speech-segmentation, lexical-retrieval and parsing skills;
- a set of reading tasks focusing on both the meaning and structural levels of the text;
- a set of translation tasks aimed at consolidation through retrieval practice;
- a set of writing tasks targeting essential writing micro-skills such as spelling, functional and positional processing, editing and communication of meaning.

Each sentence builder at the beginning of a unit contains one or more constructions which have been selected with real-life communication in mind. Each unit is built around that construction <u>but not solely on it</u>. Based on the principle that each E.P.I instructional sequence must move from modelling to production in a seamless and organic way, each unit expands on the material in each sentence builder by embedding it in texts and graded tasks which contain both familiar and unfamiliar (but comprehensible and learnable) vocabulary and structures. Through lots of careful recycling and thorough and extensive processing of the input, by the end of each unit the student has many opportunities to encounter and process the new vocabulary and patterns with material from the previous units.

Alongside the units you will find: Oral Ping Pong, One Pen One Dice & No Snakes No Ladders tasks created to practise speaking skills with an engaging and fun games that can be photocopied and played in groups of 3 students.

Important *caveats*

1) **Listening** as modelling is an essential part of E.P.I. The listening files for each listening unit can be found in the AUDIO section on Language-Gym.com - a subscription to the website is **not required** to access these.

2) **All content** in this booklet matches the content on both the **Language Gym** and **Sentence Builders** websites. For best results, we recommend a mixture of communicative, retrieval practice games, combined with Language Gym / Sentence Builders.com games and workouts, and then this booklet as the follow-up, either in class or for homework.

3) This booklet is suitable for **beginner** learners and is an ideal follow-on from **French Primary Sentence Builders – Part 1**. This booklet equates to a **CEFR A1** level, or a beginner **KS2** class. You do not need to start at the beginning, although you may want to dip in to certain units for revision/recycling.

We do hope that you and your students will find this book useful and enjoyable.

Simona, Stefano, Gianfranco & Dylan

Table of Contents

UNIT 1

Ma Famille

In this unit you will learn how to say in French:

- ✓ Who is in your immediate family
- ✓ What their name is
- ✓ How old they are
- ✓ Numbers up to 100
- ✓ *Je m'entends bien avec*

You will revisit:

- ★ Numbers up to 31
- ★ Where you live

Il y a combien de personnes dans ta famille?

Dans ma famille il y a quatre personnes:

ma mère, mon père, mon frère et moi.

THE LANGUAGE GYM

UNIT 1. MA FAMILLE
I can say who is in my immediate family, their name and age

> ### Il y a combien de personnes dans ta famille?
> *How many people are there in your family?*

			J'habite avec *I live with*		
Dans ma famille, il y a *In my family, there are*	deux 2 trois 3 quatre 4 cinq 5 six 6 sept 7 huit 8 neuf 9 dix 10	personnes *people*	Je m'entends bien avec *I get on well with* Je ne m'entends pas bien avec *I don't get on well with*	ma cousine *my cousin (f)* ma grand-mère *my grandmother* ma mère *my mother* ma sœur *my sister* ma tante *my aunt* mon cousin *my cousin (m)* mon frère *my brother* mon grand-père *my grandfather* mon oncle *my uncle* mon père *my father*	
Il s'appelle *He is called*	Gabriel Hugo Julien Louis Lucas	et il a *and he has**	onze 11 douze 12 treize 13 quatorze 14 quinze 15 seize 16 dix-sept 17 dix-huit 18 dix-neuf 19	vingt-quatre 24 vingt-cinq 25 trente 30 trente-et-un 31 trente-deux 32 quarante 40 cinquante 50 soixante 60 soixante-dix 70	ans *years old*
Elle s'appelle *She is called*	Anne Lucie Manon Sophie	et elle a *and she has**	vingt 20 vingt-et-un 21 vingt-deux 22 vingt-trois 23	quatre-vingts 80 quatre-vingt-dix 90 cent 100	

*Author's note: In French, to say your age you say *"J'ai dix ans"*, which translates literally as "I have 10 years".

Unit 1. My name and age: LISTENING

1. Listen and complete with the missing syllables

a. Ma mè _ _   f. Mon _ _ re

b. Ma tan _ _   g. Mon cou _ _ _

c. Mon _ _ _ re h. Il s'appel _ _

d. Mon on _ _ _ i. Ma cou _ _ ne

e. _ _ _ sonnes j. Dans ma fa _ _ lle

cle	si	pè	le	re
frè	te	per	mi	sin

2. Faulty Echo

e.g. Ma <u>sœur</u> a sept ans

a. Mon père s'appelle Pierre.

b. Dans ma famille, il y a trois personnes.

c. J'habite avec mon oncle.

d. Il y a combien de personnes dans ta famille?

e. Ma cousine s'appelle Isabelle.

f. Elle s'appelle Charlotte.

3. Break the flow: Draw a line between words

a. Dansmafamilleilyahuitpersonnes.

b. J'habiteavecmongrand-pèremagrand-mèreetmamère.

c. J'habiteavecmonpèremamèreetmonfrère.

d. Masœurs'appelleBéatriceetelleadixans.

e. Mononcleatrenteans.

f. Mamères'appelleMarieetjem'entendsbienavecelle.

THE LANGUAGE GYM

4. Listen and tick the correct answer ✔

		1	2	3
a.	Dans ma famille il y a	cinq personnes	six personnes	sept personnes
b.	J'habite avec	mon père	ma mère	ma grand-mère
c.	Mon frère	s'appelle Jean	s'appelle Jules	s'appelle Julien
d.	Ma sœur a	douze ans	treize ans	quatorze ans

5. Listen and write the number (1-31)

a. ____   d. ____   g. ____

b. ____   e. ____   h. ____

c. ____   f. ____   i. ____

6. Fill in the grid in English

	Family member	Age
a.		
b.		
c.		
d.		
e.		

7. Track the sounds

Listen and write down how many times you will hear the sound

1.	è	
2.	on	
3.	in	
4.	ou	
5.	an	

THE LANGUAGE GYM

4

8. Spot the Intruder

Identify and underline the word that the speaker is NOT saying

e.g. Ma mère s'appelle Anne <u>bonjour</u>.

a. Ton père s'appelle comment? Mon père s'appelle est Benoit.

b. Il y a combien de personnes dans ta famille? J'ai Il y a six personnes.

c. Dans ma famille il y a quatre personnes: mon père, ma mère, ma tante et je moi.

d. Bonjour, j'habite avec ma mère et ma famille tante. Ma tante a cinquante ans.

e. J'habite avec ma mère, mon père et mon grand-père. Je n'ai pas de mes frères.

f. Dans ma famille il y a sept huit personnes. Mon frère a dix-huit ans.

9. Listen and circle the correct number (31-100)

e.g. Quel âge a ton père?
Il a trente-neuf ans.

e.g.	49	29	39
a.	61	71	81
b.	100	50	40
c.	92	82	62
d.	44	54	74
e.	93	43	33
f.	35	36	37

10. Listen and tick: True or False?

	True	False
a. My mother is 47		
b. My brother is 16		
c. My aunt is 52		
d. My grandfather is 73		
e. My father is 60		
f. My grandmother is 70		
g. My cousin is 24		
h. My uncle is 38		

THE LANGUAGE GYM

11. Catch it, Swap it

Listen, correct the French, then translate the new word/phrase

e.g. Dans ma ~~sœur~~ *famille il y a cinq personnes.* | *e.g. family*

a. Dans ma famille il y a six personnes. | a.

b. J'habite avec mon père. Il a trente ans. | b.

c. J'habite avec ma mère. Elle a quarante ans. | c.

d. Mon frère s'appelle Paul et il a trente-sept ans. | d.

e. Ma cousine s'appelle Juliette et elle a onze ans. | e.

f. J'habite avec ma cousine. Elle a vingt-et-un ans. | f.

g. Je m'entends bien avec mon père. | g.

12. Sentence Bingo

Write 4 of the sentences into the grid. You will hear sentences in French in a RANDOM ORDER. Tick all 4 of your sentences to win bingo.

1. Ma sœur a quinze ans.
2. Mon grand-père a soixante-dix ans.
3. Ma cousine a vingt ans.
4. Mon père s'appelle Pierre.
5. J'habite avec mon père et ma mère.
6. Dans ma famille il y a deux personnes.
7. Dans ma famille il y a six personnes.
8. Ma mère a trente-deux ans.
9. Ma cousine a dix-sept ans.
10. J'habite avec mon grand-père.

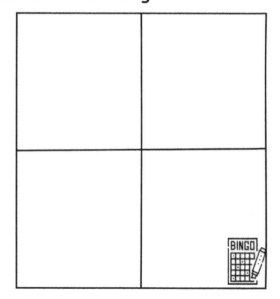

Unit 1. I can say who is in my family: READING

1. Sylla-Moles

Read and put the syllables in the cells in the correct order

pel	mè	le	Ma	An	s'ap	re	ne

a. *My mother is called Anne:* M___ m_____ s'a_____ A___n___.

ans	Mon	re	quan	cin	a	te	pè

b. *My father is 50 years old:* M___ p_____ ___ c_____ a_____.

pel	quin	Mon	Jean	le	sin	il	cou	a	et	s'ap	ans	ze

c. *My cousin is called Jean and he is 15 years old:* M___ c_____ s'_____ J_____ e___ i___ ___ q_____ a_____.

a	le	bien	y	mil	com	Il	per	dans	son	ta	nes	fa	de

d. *How many people are in your family?:* I___ ___ ___ c_____ d___ p_____ d_____ t___ f_____?

a	qua	Ma	re	grand	vingts	mè	tre	ans

e. *My grandmother is 80 years old:* M___ g_____-m_____ ___ q_____-v_____ a____.

A. Match these sentences to the pictures above

a. Ma mère a quarante-six ans.

b. Mon oncle Alfie a soixante-dix ans.

c. Je m'appelle Pierre et j'ai quinze ans.

d. Dans ma famille il y a six personnes. Ma grand-mère a soixante-douze ans.

e. Ma sœur a vingt-six ans.

f. Ma tante a trente-sept ans.

g. Mon grand-père a quatre-vingt-cinq ans.

h. Ma cousine Delphine a soixante-deux ans.

i. Mon cousin Charles a quarante-neuf ans.

j. Mon père s'appelle Jean et il a cinquante ans.

B. Read the sentences in task A again and find the French for:

a. My aunt

b. 85

c. There are 6 people

d. 26 years old

e. My cousin Charles

f. 49

g. And I am

h. Is 70 years old

i. Is 37 years old

j. My uncle

k. My sister

l. I am 15 years old

m. My father is called

n. Is 62 years old

3. Read the paragraphs and complete the tasks below

1. Salut, je m'appelle **Julien** et j'ai onze ans. J'adore ma famille, mais elle est petite. J'habite à Paris avec ma mère, ma sœur et mon grand-père. J'ai aussi un chien noir. Mon grand-père s'appelle François et il a soixante-quatorze ans. Ma mère s'appelle Louise et je m'entends bien avec elle. Quel âge a-t-elle? Elle a cinquante ans.

2. Bonjour, je m'appelle **Lucie** et j'ai neuf ans. Dans ma famille, il y a cinq personnes: mon père, ma mère, mon frère, ma sœur et moi. Mon père a quarante-neuf ans et il s'appelle Luc. Je ne m'entends pas bien avec lui. Ma mère a quarante-cinq ans et elle s'appelle Manon. Je n'ai pas d'animaux. Et toi, il y a combien de personnes dans ta famille?

A. For each sentence tick one box	True	False
a. **Julien** is 11 years old.		
b. He doesn't like his family.		
c. He has a brown dog.		
d. His grandfather is called Gabriel.		
e. **Lucie** is 12 years old.		
f. There are 5 people in her family.		
g. Her mum is 44 years old.		
h. She has a brother and a sister.		

B. Find the French for:

a. My grandfather
b. Seventy-four
c. She is 50 years old
d. My sister and me
e. In my family there are…
f. I love my family
g. I do not have pets
h. A black dog
i. How many people?
j. But it is small
k. I get on well with her
l. And you

C. Read the sentences again and decide if they describe Julien or Lucie

a. Is 9 years old.
b. Has a mum called Louise.
c. Has a brother.
d. Lives in Paris.

e. Has a small family.
f. Has a dad called Luc.
g. Doesn't have pets.
h. Has a 74-year-old grandfather.

THE LANGUAGE GYM

4. Tiles match: pair up the French and English tiles

			5. My mother is	6. 30 years old
2. My grandad	f. Mon frère	c. Mon grand-père	e. Soixante-cinq ans	d. Dans ma famille
a. Ma mère a	4. In my family	3. 65 years old	b. Trente ans	1. My brother

5. Tick or Cross

A. Read the text and tick the box if you find the words in the text, cross it if you do not find them

Bonjour, je m'appelle Juliette et j'ai quatorze ans. J'habite à Bordeaux. Dans ma famille, il y a sept personnes: ma mère, mon beau-père*, ma sœur, mes deux frères, ma grand-mère et moi. J'aime ma famille car elle est grande. J'ai aussi un chat gris qui s'appelle Tigrou. Ma mère a quarante-cinq ans et mon beau-père a quarante-huit ans. Je m'entends très bien avec ma sœur. Elle s'appelle Charlotte, elle a dix-sept ans, et elle parle très bien français. [*beau-père = stepfather]

		✓	✗
a.	J'aime		
b.	Treize ans		
c.	Elle s'appelle		
d.	Mon grand-père et moi		
e.	A grey dog		
f.	I get on really well		
g.	48 years old		
h.	Speaks French very well		

B. Find the French in the text above

a. My grandmother and me. _____

b. My mother is 45 years old. _____

c. There are seven people. _____

d. Also, I have a grey cat. _____

e. She is 17 years old. _____

6. Language Detective

* <u>Je m'appelle</u> **Jean**. J'ai onze ans. J'habite à Nice avec ma famille. Je m'entends bien avec mon frère Louis. Il a huit ans. Je ne m'entends pas bien avec ma mère. Elle a trente-neuf ans. Je n'ai pas d'animaux.

* Je m'appelle **Marie**. J'ai douze ans. Dans ma famille il y a sept personnes: mon père, ma mère, ma sœur, mon frère, mon grand-père, ma grand-mère, et moi. Je m'entends bien avec mon grand-père. Il a soixante-douze ans. Je ne m'entends pas bien avec mon père. Il a quarante-quatre ans.

* Salut, je m'appelle **Nicolas**. Mon anniversaire est le cinq juillet. J'ai un chien blanc qui s'appelle Rocky. Dans ma famille il y a quatre personnes: ma belle-mère, mon père, ma sœur et moi. J'ai aussi trois cousins.

* Bonjour, je m'appelle **Martine**. J'habite à Lyon et je parle espagnol et français. J'ai une grande famille. Il y a six personnes. Je m'entends très bien avec ma sœur aînée. Elle a vingt-cinq ans. Je ne m'entends pas bien avec ma mère. Elle a cinquante ans.

A. Find someone who...

a. ...has a 72-year-old grandfather.

b. ...was born on the 5th July.

c. ...has a 44-year-old father.

d. ...has a 50-year-old mum.

e. ...has a family of 6 people.

f. ...speaks Spanish and French.

g. ...has three cousins.

h. ...doesn't have pets.

i. ...doesn't get on well with their father.

B. Find and underline the French in the text. One box is not mentioned!

My name is	She is 25 years old	There are 6 people
I have a big family	I get on well	I am 11 years old
A white dog	My older sister	20th June
With my mother	44 years old	I don't get on well

THE LANGUAGE GYM

7. Square This!

Reorder the sentences in the square to translate the paragraph below. Number them 1 to 15. Then write out the paragraph in French.

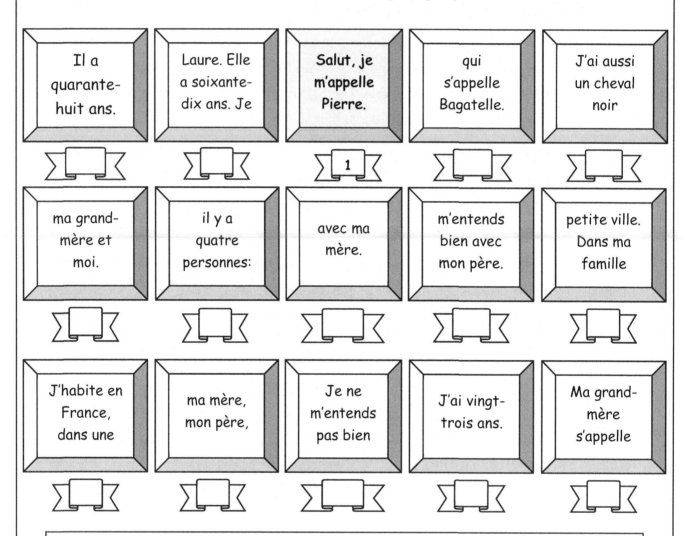

Il a quarante-huit ans.	Laure. Elle a soixante-dix ans. Je	**Salut, je m'appelle Pierre.**	qui s'appelle Bagatelle.	J'ai aussi un cheval noir
		1		
ma grand-mère et moi.	il y a quatre personnes:	avec ma mère.	m'entends bien avec mon père.	petite ville. Dans ma famille
J'habite en France, dans une	ma mère, mon père,	Je ne m'entends pas bien	J'ai vingt-trois ans.	Ma grand-mère s'appelle

Hello, my name is Pierre. I am 23 years old. I live in France, in a small city. In my family there are four people: my mother, my father, my grandmother and me. My grandmother is called Laure. She is 70 years old. I get on well with my father. He is 48 years old. I don't get on well with my mother. I also have a black horse called Bagatelle.

Unit 1. My name and age: VOCABULARY BUILDING

1. Spelling: fill in the missing letters

a. I__ __ tr__ __z__ a__ __.   *He is 13 years old.*

b. Q__ __ __ __ __t__-__ __u__ __n__.   *42 years.*

c. E__ __ __ s'__ __ __e__ __ __.   *She is called.*

d. I__ s'ap__e__l__ c__m__e__t?   *What is his name?*

e. Qu__ __ â__ __ a-t-e__ __ __?   *How old is she?*

f. D__ __ __ __ m__ fa__i__ __e i__ y __... *In my family there is/are...*

2. Anagrams: unscramble the French

a. onM rpèe a qaantrue asn   *My father is 40 years old.*

___ ___ ___   ___ ___ ___ ___   ___   ___ ___ ___ ___ ___ ___ ___ ___ ___   ___ ___ ___.

b. Dnsa am flemila il y a edxu ernnspoes   *In my family there are 2 people.*

___ ___ ___ ___   ___ ___   ___ ___ ___ ___ ___ ___ ___   ___ ___   ___   ___   ___ ___ ___ ___

___ ___ ___ ___ ___ ___ ___ ___ ___.

c. aM surœ ps'paelle niDalele   *My sister is called Danielle.*

___ ___   ___ ___ ___ ___ ___   ___'___ ___ ___ ___ ___ ___ ___   ___ ___ ___ ___ ___ ___ ___ ___.

3. Gapped translation: fill in the missing words

a. J'habite avec trois personnes: ma mère, ma sœur et ma grand-mère.

I_____ with three _____: my mother, my sister and my _____.

b. J'habite avec ma tante qui s'appelle Giselle et elle a cinquante-et-un ans.

I live with my _____ who is _____ Giselle and she is _____ years old.

c. J'habite à Londres avec mon père. Il s'appelle Paul et il a trente ans.

I live in London _____ my _____. ____ is called Paul and is _____ years old.

THE LANGUAGE GYM

4. No vowels: fill in the missing letters

a. I live with my sister and my father.

J'h__b__t__ __v__c m__ s__ __ __r __t m__n p__r__.

b. My grandmother is called Angèle.

M__ gr__nd-m__r__ s'__pp__ ll__ __ng__l__.

c. My uncle is thirty-five years old.

M__n __ncl__ __ tr__nt__-c__nq __ns.

5. No consonants: fill in the missing letters

a. In my family there are seven people.

__a__ __ __a __a__i__ __e i__ __a __e__ __ __e__ __o__ __e__.

b. I get on well with my mother and father.

__e __'é__ __e__ __ __ __ie__ a__e__ __a __è__e e__ __o__ __è__e.

c. I live with my aunt. She is called Madeleine.

__'__a__i__e a__e__ __a __a__ __e. E__ __e __'a__ __e__ __e __a__e__ei__e.

6. Split sentences: match the parts to create sentences

1. Elle a	a. ma mère	1	
2. Mon frère	b. personnes dans ta famille?	2	
3. Ta sœur	c. s'appelle Michel	3	
4. Dans ma famille il y a	d. vingt ans	4	
5. J'habite avec	e. s'appelle comment?	5	
6. Il y a combien de	f. trois personnes	6	
7. J'ai quarante-	g. trois ans	7	

THE LANGUAGE GYM

Unit 1. My name and age: WRITING

7. Fill in the gaps

a. Bonjour, je m'appelle Suzanne. _____ à Toulouse, je _____ italien et français. _____ une grande famille. Il y a sept personnes. Je _____ très bien avec ma _____ aînée. Elle a _____ ans. Je ne m'entends pas ____ avec ma mère.

treize	J'habite	J'ai	sœur	parle	bien	m'entends

b. Salut, je m'appelle Jules et j'ai douze ____. J'_____ ma famille, mais elle est petite. J'habite à Strasbourg avec ___ mère, ma sœur et mon grand-père. ____ aussi un chien noir. Mon grand-père _____ Florent. Il a soixante-_____ ans et je m'entends bien avec ____.

lui	ma	J'ai	ans	s'appelle	adore	quatorze

8. Sentence Puzzle

Put the French words in the correct order

a. famille Dans personnes ma il cinq y a
    In my family there are five people.

b. dans y a personnes famille combien de Il ta ?
    How many people are there in your family?

c. s'appelle Ma ans Danielle et elle a sœur quarante-deux
    My sister is called Danielle and she is 42 years old.

d. avec Je mon bien Bernard père, il m'entends s'appelle
    I get on well with my father, his name is Bernard.

e. mère ma avec à J'habite Marseille a ans trente-neuf Elle
    I live with my mother in Marseille. She is 39 years old.

9. Faulty Translation: write the correct English version

e.g. J'ai <u>dix</u> ans. $\Longrightarrow$ I am <u>11</u> years old.

e.g. I am 10 years old.

a. Elle a sept ans. $\Longrightarrow$ He is 7 years old.

a.

b. Il s'appelle comment? $\Longrightarrow$ What's your name?

b.

c. Quel âge a-t-elle? $\Longrightarrow$ How old are you?

c.

d. Je m'appelle Nathan. $\Longrightarrow$ Her name is Nathan.

d.

10. Phrase-level Translation. How would you write it in French?

a. She is 30 years old. _____

b. His name is... _____

c. What's her name? _____

d. Her name is... _____

e. He is 20 years old. _____

f. How old are you? _____

11. Sentence Jumble: unscramble the sentences

a. mère mon Marguerite père s'appelle Ma et Paul s'appelle

_____

b. dans de y famille personnes Il a ta combien ?

_____

c. frère Claude ans et il s'appelle a vingt-sept Mon

_____

d. frère s'appelle comment Ton ?

_____

12. Guided Translation

a. I__ y __ c_____ d__ p_____ d_____ t__ f_____?

How many people are there in your family?

b. J__ m'_____ b_____ a_____ m__ s_____ e__ m__ m_____.

I get on well with my sister and my mother.

c. M__ g_____-_____ s'_____ P____ e__ i__ __ q_____-v_____ a___.

My grandfather is called Paul and he is 80 years old.

d. D_____ m__ f_____ i__ __ __ d_____ p_____: m___ p_____ e__ m___.

In my family there are two people: my father and I.

13. Tangled Translation

a. Write the French words in English to complete the translation

My name is Catherine. **J'ai** eleven **ans.** I live **à Strasbourg,** I like it **parce que c'est joli.** In my family **il y a quatre** people: **ma** mother, **mon** father, **mon** brother **et moi.** I get on well **avec mon frère,** he **a** eight **ans, mais** I don't get on **bien** with my **mère.** She **a trente-nine ans. J'ai un** white dog **qui s'appelle** Tchoupi.

b. Write the English words in French to complete the translation

My name is Christine et j'ai quatorze **years old.** J'habite **in** Dijon et **I speak** anglais et **French, but** je ne parle pas espagnol. Dans **my family there are** cinq personnes: **my father,** ma mère, ma sœur, **my grandfather** et ma tante. **I get on well** avec ma tante, **she a thirty-three** ans, **but** je ne m'entends pas bien **with** mon père, **he a forty seven** ans. **I don't have** d'animaux.

THE LANGUAGE GYM

14. Rock Climbing

Starting from the bottom, pick one chunk from each row to translate the sentences below.

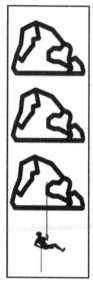

ans.	avec mon oncle et ma tante.	quinze ans.	quarante-deux ans.	ma sœur et moi.
Je m'entends bien	Il a quatre-vingt-trois	ma mère, mon père,	Elle a	et il a
avec ma sœur.	il y a cinq personnes:	s'appelle Robert	bien avec mon grand-père.	famille en France.
Dans ma famille	Mon père	Je m'entends bien	Je ne m'entends pas	J'habite avec ma
a.	b.	c.	d.	e.

a. In my family there are five people: my mother, my father, my sister, and me.

_____

b. My father is called Robert and he is forty-two years old.

_____

c. I get on well with my sister. She is fifteen years old.

_____

d. I don't get on well with my grandfather. He is 83 years old.

_____

e. I live with my family in France. I get on well with my uncle and my aunt.

_____

THE LANGUAGE GYM

No Snakes No Ladders

7 Jules a quinze ans	6 Je n'ai pas de frères	5 Mon père, ma mère et mon frère	4 Je m'entends bien avec mon oncle	3 Quel âge as-tu?	2 Cinq personnes	1 Dans ma famille il y a
8 Je ne m'entends pas avec ma tante	9 Ma sœur s'appelle Anne	10 Mon cousin a douze ans	11 Mon oncle a trente-six ans	12 Mon père s'appelle Jean	13 Dans ma famille il y a six personnes	14 Il s'appelle Philippe
23 Trente-et-un ans	22 Elle a soixante-dix-neuf ans	21 Il a vingt-deux ans	20 Je m'entends bien avec ma cousine	19 Elle s'appelle Sophie	18 Quatre-vingt-quinze ans	17 Soixante, soixante-dix
24 Marie a quatorze ans	25 Dans ma famille il y a trois personnes	26 Ma tante s'appelle Charlotte	27 Quatre-vingts, quatre-vingt-dix	28 Il a dix-huit ans	29 Je m'entends avec ma famille	30 Elle a cinquante ans

DÉPART

15 Ma mère a quarante ans

16 J'ai deux sœurs

ARRIVÉE

No Snakes No Ladders

7 Jules is 15 years old	6 I don't have brothers	5 My father, my mother and my brother	4 I get on well with my uncle	3 How old are you?	2 Five people	1 In my family there are	DÉPART
8 I don't get on with my aunt	9 My sister is called Anne	10 My cousin (m) is 12 years old	11 My uncle is 36 years old	12 My father is called Jean	13 In my family there are 6 people	14 He is called Philippe	15 My mother is 40 years old
23 31 years old	22 She is 79 years old	21 He is 22 years old	20 I get on well with my cousin (f)	19 She is called Sophie	18 95 years	17 Sixty, seventy	16 I have 2 sisters
24 Marie is 14 years old	25 In my family there are 3 people	26 My aunt is called Charlotte	27 Eighty, ninety	28 He 18 years old	29 I get on with my family	30 She is 50 years old	ARRIVÉE

THE LANGUAGE GYM

UNIT 2

COMMENT ES-TU?

In this unit you will learn how to say in French:

✓ What type of personality you/others have
✓ Quantifiers/Intensifiers

You will revisit:

★ Masculine/Feminine adjectival agreement
★ Verb *être (je suis - tu es - il est - elle est)*

Comment es-tu?

Normalement je suis drôle et gentille.

THE LANGUAGE GYM

UNIT 2. Comment es-tu?

I can say what type of personality myself and others have

Comment es-tu? *What are you like?*

En général *In general*	je suis *I am* je ne suis pas *I am not*	assez *quite* très *very* un peu *a little*	actif/ve *active* bavard/e *talkative* gentil/le *kind* heureux/reuse *happy* intelligent/e *intelligent* optimiste *optimistic* patient/e *patient*
Je m'entends bien avec *I get on well with* **Je ne m'entends pas bien avec** *I do not get on well with*	mon ami *my friend* mon frère *my brother* mon grand-père *my grandfather* mon père *my father*	car il est *because he is* mais il est *but he is* cependant, il est *however, he is*	drôle *funny* généreux *generous* méchant *mean* paresseux *lazy* pénible *annoying* sévère *strict* sympathique *nice* têtu *stubborn* timide *shy*
	mon amie *my friend* ma grand-mère *my grandmother* ma mère *my mother* ma sœur *my sister*	car elle est *because she is* mais elle est *but she is* cependant, elle est *however, she is*	drôle généreuse méchante paresseuse pénible sévère sympathique têtue timide

Unit 2. Personality: LISTENING

1. Listen and complete with the missing syllable

a. Pa _ _ _ _ _

b. Sympa _ _ _ que

c. Ba _ _ _ de

d. _ _ néreux

e. Drô _ _

f. Intelli _ _ _ te

g. Mé _ _ _ _ te

h. Pé _ _ ble

i. Heu _ _ _ _

j. Sé _ _ re

| reux le chan var vè |
| thi gé ni gen tient |

2. Faulty Echo

e.g. *Mon frère est un peu méchant.*

a. Mon père est très sympathique.

b. En général je suis patient.

c. Je m'entends bien avec ma tante.

d. Ma mère est très intelligente.

e. Mon ami est un peu timide.

f. Ma sœur est bavarde et têtue.

g. En général je suis assez heureux.

h. Comment es-tu? Je suis gentille.

3. Break the flow: Draw a line between words

a. Jem'entendsbienavecmamèrecarelleestdrôle.

b. Jenem'entendspasbienavecmongrand-pèrecarilestsévère.

c. Monpèreesttrèsintelligent,maisunpeutimide.

d. Engénéraljem'entendsbienavecmasœuraînée.

e. Monamies'appelleMélanie.Elleesttrèssympathiqueetgénéreuse.

f. Jenem'entendspasbienavecmonamicarilestparesseux.

g. Engénéraljenesuispasoptimiste,maisjesuisgentil.

THE LANGUAGE GYM

4. Listen and tick the correct answer

		1	2	3
a.	En général	je suis sympathique	elle est sympathique	il est sympathique
b.	Mon père est	paresseux	patient	intelligent
c.	Mon amie est	généreuse	drôle	gentille
d.	Je suis très	bavard	bavarde	gentil
e.	Ma grand-mère est	un peu sévère	assez sévère	très sévère

5. Spot the Intruder

Identify and underline the word that the speaker is NOT saying

> **e.g.** Je m'entends bien avec ma <u>suis</u> mère car elle est sympathique.

a. Comment es-tu? En général je suis très assez patient et drôle.

b. Je ne m'entends pas bien avec ma grand-mère car elle est têtue mais et sévère.

c. Je m'entends bien avec mon ami Charles car il est paresseux sympathique.

d. Je ne suis pas très intelligent, mais je m'entends suis très actif et heureux.

e. Mon frère assez est un peu timide, mais il n'est pas pénible.

f. Mon ami Adeline est très bavarde, car mais elle est gentille.

6. Listen and tick: True or False?

	True	False
a. My mother is friendly.		
b. My brother is kind.		
c. My friend Hugo is funny.		
d. My grandfather is strict.		
e. My father is generous.		
f. My grandmother is mean.		
g. My cousin Chloé is shy.		
h. In general, I am kind.		
i. I get on well with my mum because she is talkative.		
j. I don't get on well with my uncle because he is lazy.		

7. Fill in the grid in English

e.g. My uncle	*kind, funny*
a. I am	
b. My father	
c. _____	_____, shy
d. My grandfather	
e. My mother	
f. _____	lazy, _____
g. My friend	
h. My cousin	
i. My brother	
j. _____	kind, _____

8. Narrow Listening. Gapped translation

a. In general, I am quite _____ and _____. I ___ _____ _____ with my _____ because she is _____, but at times she is a little_____. I don't get on _____ with my _____ because he is _____.

b. What are you like? I am not _____, but I am _____. I get on well with my _____ because he is _____ _____. However, he is not _____. I don't _____ ___ well with my _____ Pauline because she is _____ _____.

25

THE LANGUAGE GYM

9. Catch it, Swap it

Listen, correct the French, then translate the new word/phrase

e.g. Mon grand-père est drôle mais un peu ~~sympathique~~ **sévère**.

e.g. strict	

a. En général, je suis assez optimiste.

a.

b. Comment es-tu? Normalement, je suis têtu et actif.

b.

c. Je m'entends bien avec mon cousin car il est méchant.

c.

d. Mon oncle est assez généreux, mais un peu pénible.

d.

e. Mon amie Céline est très gentille, mais elle n'est pas drôle.

e.

f. Je m'entends bien avec ma sœur car elle est sérieuse.

f.

g. Je suis un peu actif, cependant, je ne suis pas patient.

g.

10. Sentence Bingo

Write 4 of the sentences into the grid. You will hear sentences in French in a RANDOM ORDER. Tick all 4 of your sentences to win bingo.

1. Mon frère est très généreux.
2. Ma sœur aînée est un peu timide.
3. Je m'entends bien avec mon grand-père.
4. En général, je suis assez drôle.
5. Normalement, mon cousin est paresseux.
6. Ma tante est assez sympathique.
7. Je ne m'entends pas bien avec mon ami.
8. Ma mère est assez généreuse.
9. Je m'entends bien avec mes parents.
10. Je ne suis pas têtue car je suis patiente.

11. Listening Slalom

Listen and pick the equivalent English words from each column – drawing a line as you follow the speaker

e.g. Ma sœur est optimiste et heureuse, mais un peu méchante.

My sister is optimistic and happy, but a little mean.

You could colour in the boxes for each sentence in a different colour and read out the sentence in French

e.g.	My sister	I am shy,	she is patient	I am stubborn
a.	My brother	I am not	and happy, but	very talkative
b.	In general,	is optimistic	because he is mean	and very kind
c.	I get on well with	is funny	but at times	a little mean
d.	I don't get on well with	my mother because	and very nice	but strict
e.	My grandfather	my father	and generous	but quite lazy
f.	Normally,	is very intelligent	active, but I am	and he is not funny

THE LANGUAGE GYM

Unit 2. I can describe personality: READING

1. Sylla-Moles

Read and put the syllables in the cells in the correct order

as	Je	et	sez	suis	tient	pa	reux	heu

a. *I am quite patient and happy:* J__ s____ a_____ p_____ e__ h_____.

est	tê	pè	gen	grand	til	re	Mon	mais	tu

b. *My grandfather is kind, but stubborn:* M___ g_____-p_____ e___ g_____, m_____ t_____.

un	mi	te	peu	Ma	ac	est	ve	tan	et	ti	de	ti

c. *My aunt is a little active and shy:* M__ t_____ e___ u___ p_____ a_____ et t_____.

vard	mi	pas	a	mais	est	til	ba	gen	Mon	il	n'est

d. *My friend is not talkative, but he's kind:* M___ a_____ n'___ p___ b_____, m_____ i__ e___ g_____.

mè	bien	elle	m'en	ma	Je	mais	tends	vec	a	re	vè	est	sé	re

e. *I get on well with my mother, but she is strict:* J__ m'_____ b_____ a____ m__ m_____, m_____ e___ e___ s_____.

THE LANGUAGE GYM

2. Read the paragraphs and complete the tasks below

1. J'habite à Nantes avec mon père, ma mère et ma grand-mère. En général, je m'entends bien avec ma mère car elle est généreuse et très gentille, mais quelquefois elle est sévère. Ma grand-mère s'appelle Anne et elle a soixante-huit ans. Elle est très sympathique et bavarde. Je ne m'entends pas bien avec mon père car il est un peu têtu. Il a quarante-huit ans. **(Philippe)**

2. Salut, en général je suis assez drôle et optimiste. Dans ma famille il y a quatre personnes. Je m'entends bien avec mon père car il est patient et actif, mais quelquefois il est paresseux. Ma sœur a quatorze ans et elle est un peu paresseuse. Je ne m'entends pas bien avec mon frère car il est timide. Cependant, il est intelligent.
Et toi, comment es-tu? **(Margot)**

A. For each sentence tick one box	True	False
a. **Philippe** gets on well with his mum.		
b. His mum is generous, but strict.		
c. His gran is mean and lazy.		
d. Philippe's dad is very stubborn.		
e. **Margot,** in general, is kind and funny.		
f. Her dad is patient and active.		
g. Her sister is 15 and she is shy.		
h. She doesn't get on well with her brother because he is chatty.		

B. Find the French for:

a. She is very nice
b. She is strict
c. She is 68
d. I don't get on well with...
e. In general
f. He is a little stubborn
g. She is a little lazy
h. In my family there are...
i. However, he is intelligent
j. What are you like?
k. I am quite funny
l. Sometimes he is lazy

C. Read the sentences again and decide if they refer to Philippe or Margot

a. Dad is 48 years old.
b. Gets on well with mum.
c. Sister is 14 years old.
d. Is optimistic.
e. Mum is very kind.
f. Brother is shy.
g. Grandmother is chatty.
h. Has a family of 4 people.

THE LANGUAGE GYM

3. Tiles Match. Pair them up

1. A little chatty	6. She is nice	4. Very happy	d. Très heureux	e. Elle est sympathique
f. Ma mère est	5. I am very funny	a. Je m'entends	c. Un peu bavard	2. My mother is

Top row:
3. I get on | b. Je suis très drôle

4. Tick or Cross

A. Read the text and tick the box if you find the words in the text, cross it if you do not find them

Salut, je m'appelle **Jean** et j'ai treize ans. J'habite à Lille avec ma famille. En général, je suis assez actif et heureux. Je m'entends bien avec ma sœur car elle est drôle et sympathique, mais je ne m'entends pas bien avec mon grand-père car il est un peu méchant. Ma mère s'appelle Anne et elle a quarante-neuf ans. Normalement, elle est généreuse et gentille. Cependant, quelquefois, elle est un peu têtue. J'aime mon père car il est assez intelligent et optimiste, mais quelquefois, il est un peu paresseux.

		✓	✗
a.	Assez intelligent		
b.	Treize ans		
c.	Mais quelquefois		
d.	Ma grand-mère car		
e.	Normally she is		
f.	A little shy		
g.	Is quite intelligent		
h.	Funny and kind		
i.	She is 49 years old		

B. Find the French in the texts above

a. She is 49 years old. _____
b. She is generous and kind. _____
c. In general, I am quite active. _____
d. However, at times she is… _____
e. Because he is a little mean. _____

THE LANGUAGE GYM

5. Language Detective

★ Comment es-tu? <u>En général</u>, je suis assez gentille. J'ai douze ans et je suis très active. Je m'entends bien avec mon frère cadet François car il est drôle. Je m'entends bien aussi avec ma mère. Elle a quarante ans. Elle est patiente et optimiste. **Laure**

★ J'ai onze ans. Dans ma famille il y a cinq personnes. Je m'entends bien avec ma belle-mère car elle est drôle et sympathique. Je ne m'entends pas bien avec ma grand-mère car elle est très bavarde et sévère. **Julien**

★ Salut, je m'appelle **Serge**. Je vis dans une petite ville dans le sud de la France. Je m'entends bien avec mon amie Alice car elle est très intelligente et drôle. J'aime aussi mon père car il est heureux et généreux. Cependant, il est un peu timide.

★ Comment es-tu? Normalement, je suis très patient. J'ai quinze ans et je m'entends bien avec ma sœur aînée Isabelle. Elle est très active et aussi sympathique. Je ne m'entends pas bien avec ma tante. Elle a trente-cinq ans et elle est un peu têtue. **Luc**

A. Find someone who…

a. …is normally very patient.

b. …lives in the south of France.

c. …has a young brother who is very funny.

d. …doesn't get on well with their gran.

e. …has a 40-year-old mum.

f. …doesn't get on well with their aunt.

g. …has a friend who is very intelligent.

h. …has an older sister who is very active.

i. …has a talkative grandmother.

B. Find and underline the French in the text. One box is not mentioned!

In general	She is 35 years old	I live in a small town
She is patient	I get on well	with my stepmother
However,	He is a bit shy	very talkative and strict
Also I like	He is kind and generous	I also get on well

THE LANGUAGE GYM

6. Square This!

Reorder the sentences in the square to translate the paragraph below.
Number them 1 to 15. Then write out the paragraph in French.

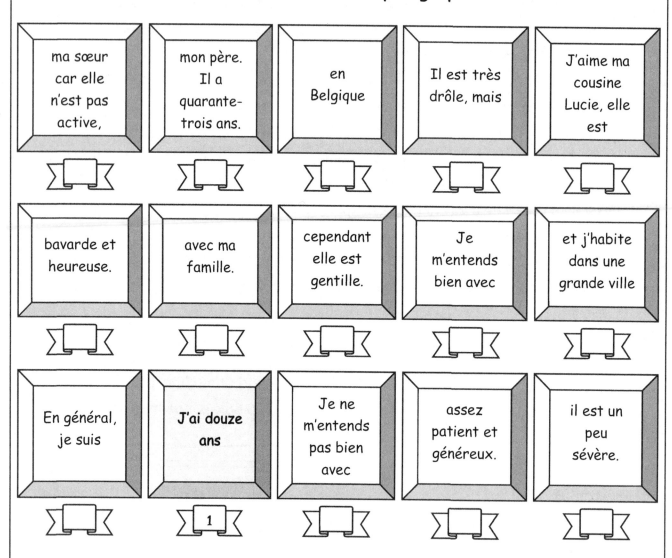

ma sœur car elle n'est pas active,	mon père. Il a quarante-trois ans.	en Belgique	Il est très drôle, mais	J'aime ma cousine Lucie, elle est
bavarde et heureuse.	avec ma famille.	cependant elle est gentille.	Je m'entends bien avec	et j'habite dans une grande ville
En général, je suis	J'ai douze ans [1]	Je ne m'entends pas bien avec	assez patient et généreux.	il est un peu sévère.

I am 12 years old and I live in a big city in Belgium with my family. In general, I am quite patient and generous. I get on well with my father. He is 43 years old. He is very funny, but he is a bit strict. I don't get on well with my sister because she is not active however, she is kind. I like my cousin Lucie. She is talkative and happy.

Unit 2. Personality: WRITING

1. Spelling

a. J__ s_____ t___s h__r_u__.   *I am very happy.*

b. E_____ e_t a_____z a_t_____.   *She is quite active.*

c. J__ n_ s_____ p_s p____i_n_e.   *I am not patient.*

d. C____m__nt e__-t__? J__ s__i_ d__ôl__.   *What are you like? I am funny.*

e. Il e____ sé____r__ e__ pa_e__s____x.   *He is strict and lazy.*

f. M__ m_____ e____ g__n__i__e.   *My mother is kind.*

2. Anagrams

a. oMn ganrd-èpre tes rèst svèéer.   *My grandfather is very strict.*

____ _____ ____-_____ ____ _____ _____.

b. nMo mai ets dtiiem, aims heuxure.   *My friend is shy, but happy.*

____ ____ _____ _____ ____ _____ _____.

c. aM taten set reeénéugs te ôrlde.   *My aunt is generous and funny.*

__ _____ ___ _____ __ _____.

3. Gapped Translation

a. En général, je suis assez optimiste et patiente. Cependant, je suis timide.

In general, __ ___ quite optimistic and _____. _____, I am shy.

b. Je m'entends bien avec ma grand-mère car elle est sympathique et bavarde.

I ____ ___ _____ with my _____ because she is nice and _____.

c. Je ne m'entends pas bien avec ma sœur car elle est têtue et paresseuse.

I ____ get on ____ with my _____ because she is _____ and _____.

THE LANGUAGE GYM

4. No Vowels

a. My friend Pierre is a little shy.

M__ n __ m__ P__ __ rr__ __ st __ n p___ t__ m__ d__.

b. I am intelligent and funny.

J__ s___ s __ nt__ ll__ g__ nt __t dr__ l__.

c. My brother is quite talkative.

M__ n fr__ r__ __ st __ ss__ z b__ v__ rd.

5. No Consonants

a. My grandfather is generous.

__ o__ ___ a___ -__ è__ e e___ __ é__ é__ eu__.

b. What are you like? I am very stubborn.

__ o___ e___ e__ -__ u? __ e __ui__ ___ è__ __ ê__ u.

c. My sister is talkative and funny.

__ a __ œu__ e___ __ a__ a___ e e__ ___ ô__ e.

6. Split Sentences

1. Je m'entends bien	a. je suis patient et heureux
2. En général	b. avec ma sœur
3. Je suis assez	c. Je suis assez actif
4. Ma mère	d. intelligente et gentille
5. Mon cousin Charles	e. mais assez sévère
6. Comment es-tu?	f. est sympathique
7. Je suis généreuse,	g. est un peu paresseux

1	
2	
3	
4	
5	
6	
7	

THE LANGUAGE GYM

7. Fill in the gaps

a. Salut, j'ai treize _____ et j'habite à Paris. En général, je _____ assez actif et
_____. Je m'_____ bien avec ma mère car elle est _____,
mais quelquefois un _____ sévère. Je ne m'entends pas bien avec mon grand-père
car il est très _____ et méchant.

drôle	peu	ans	généreuse	entends	têtu	suis

b. Comment es-tu? Normalement, je suis très heureuse et _____ patiente. Je
m'entends bien avec ma famille et j'ai deux _____. J'aime mon père _____ il est
intelligent. Cependant, il est un peu _____. Je _____ m'entends pas bien
avec ma _____ Amandine car elle est très _____.

animaux	ne	paresseux	timide	sœur	assez	car

8. Sentence Puzzle
Put the French words in the correct order

a. m'entends Je il mon bien gentil frère avec car est
   I get on well with my brother because he is kind.

b. es-tu assez? Je intelligent suis Comment drôle et
   What are you like? I am intelligent and quite funny.

c. ne pas elle avec est ma bien grand-mère Je car sévère m'entends
   I don't get on well with my grandmother because she is strict.

d. cousine est paresseuse est sympathique, cependant très Sarah elle Ma
   My cousin Sarah is very nice, however she is lazy.

e. ne généreux pas Je mais je suis très suis bavard patient et
   I am not patient, but I am very talkative and generous.

THE LANGUAGE GYM

9. Faulty Translation: write the correct English version

e.g. Je suis <u>très</u> paresseux. ⟹ I am <u>quite</u> lazy. | *e.g.* I am very lazy.

a. Elle est sympathique et drôle. ⟹ She is shy and funny. | a.

b. Mon père est têtu. ⟹ My father is happy. | b.

c. Ma tante est très bavarde. ⟹ My aunt is very patient. | c.

d. Il est assez pénible. ⟹ He is very active. | d.

e. Je ne suis pas très généreux. ⟹ I am very generous. | e.

10. Phrase-level Translation. How would you write it in French?

a. She is very intelligent. _____

b. I get on well with… _____

c. My grandmother is a little strict. _____

d. What are you like? _____

e. Because he is quite shy. _____

f. However, I am patient. _____

11. Sentence Jumble: unscramble the sentence

a. bien drôle elle avec ma sœur aînée m'entends car est Je

_____

b. grand-mère Ma sympathique très est active elle et est

_____

c. bien père Je avec mon généreux m'entends car il est

_____

d. général, je un bavard En heureux suis et peu

_____

12. Guided Translation

a. C_____ e__-t__? N_____ j__ s_____ t_____ h_____.

What are you like? Normally I am very happy.

b. J__ m'_____ b____ a____ m__ c_____ c___ e____ e___ d_____.

I get on well with my cousin because she is funny.

c. M__ g____-m___ e___ i_____, m____ q_____ e___ e___ s_____.

My grandmother is intelligent, but at times she is strict.

d. J__ m'_____ J____. J__ n__ s____ p__ t_____, m___ j__ s____ t___.

My name is Jean. I am not shy, but I am stubborn.

13. Tangled Translation

a. Write the French words in English to complete the translation

I am 12 years old and **j'habite en France** with my family. **En général**, I am **heureux**. I get on well

avec ma mère. She is 40 years old. **Elle s'appelle Hélène** and she is very patient, **mais**

quelquefois, she is **un peu paresseuse. Je ne m'entends pas bien avec** my brother because **il est**

méchant, however he is active. **J'aime aussi ma grand-mère car** she is optimistic.

b. Write the English words in French to complete the translation

My name is Nathalie, j'ai quinze ans **and I live in Canada. In general,** je suis gentille **and happy.**
Je m'entends bien **with my sister Louise.** J'aime Louise **because she is very** active et forte. **I
don't get on well with** ma sœur Isabelle car elle est très bavarde **and she is a bit stubborn.**
J'aime **my grandmother Thérèse** car **she is quite active, and she is** très intelligente. **I also
like my cousin Antoine,** mais il est timide.

THE LANGUAGE GYM

14. Rock Climbing

Starting from the bottom, pick one chunk from each row to translate the sentences below.

	a.	b.	c.	d.	e.
	un peu paresseuse.	mais elle est un peu pénible.	et gentil.	et généreux.	très bavard.
	et aussi	Elle est très sympathique, mais	mais il est très intelligent	car elle est drôle,	je suis assez patient
	trente-deux ans.	avec mon père,	bien avec ma sœur	optimiste. Cependant,	je suis assez actif
	Je m'entends	En général,	Je ne m'entends pas bien	Ma tante a	Je ne suis pas très
	a.	b.	c.	d.	e.

a. I get on well with my sister because she is funny, but she is a little annoying.

_____

b. In general, I am quite active and also very talkative.

_____

c. I don't get on well with my father, but he is very intelligent and generous.

_____

d. My aunt is 32 years old. She is very nice, but a little lazy.

_____

e. I am not very optimistic. However, I am quite patient and kind.

_____

THE LANGUAGE GYM

15. Staircase Translation

Starting from the top, translate each chunk into French.

Write the sentences in the grid below.

a.	I am kind	and intelligent.				
b.	My mother	is very generous	and patient.			
c.	I get on well	with my cousin Léa	because she is funny	and she is not mean.		
d.	My name is Charles. I am a little	shy because I am not	very talkative.	I like my uncle, but	he is annoying.	
e.	Anne, what are you like?	In general,	I am active	and happy,	but sometimes	I am lazy.

Answers / Réponses

a.	
b.	
c.	
d.	
e.	

🏆 Challenge / Défi

Can you create 2 more sentences using the words in the staircase grid above?

☆	
☆	

 THE LANGUAGE GYM

One pen One dice

Play in pairs. You only have 1 pen and 1 dice.

One person has the pen and starts translating the sentence into **English**. The other person rolls the dice until they roll a 6, they swap the pen and translate. The winner is the person who finishes translating all the sentences first.

1. En général, je suis très bavarde.	
2. Je m'entends bien avec mon frère.	
3. Je ne suis pas patient, mais je suis très gentil.	
4. Ma mère est un peu sévère.	
5. Mon père est intelligent et optimiste.	
6. Ma grand-mère est timide, mais sympathique.	
7. Comment es-tu? Je suis heureux.	
8. Mon frère n'est pas paresseux.	
9. Mon amie Léa est généreuse.	
10. Mon grand-père est paresseux mais intelligent.	

One pen One dice

Play in pairs. You only have 1 pen and 1 dice.

One person has the pen and starts translating the sentence into **French**. The other person rolls the dice until they roll a 6, they swap the pen and translate. The winner is the person who finishes translating all the sentences first.

1. In general I am very talkative (f).	
2. I get on well with my brother.	
3. I am not patient, but I am very kind (m).	
4. My mother is a little strict.	
5. My father is intelligent and optimistic.	
6. My grandmother is shy, but nice.	
7. What are you like? I am happy (m).	
8. My brother is not lazy.	
9. My friend Léa is generous.	
10. My grandfather is lazy but intelligent.	

THE LANGUAGE GYM

UNIT 3

LES YEUX ET LES CHEVEUX

In this unit you will learn how to describe in French:

- ✓ Eyes (colour and size)
- ✓ Hair (colour, length, style)
- ✓ Other facial features
- ✓ Use of verb *'Être' (je suis - tu es – il/elle est)*
  To be (I am - you are - he/she/it is)

You will revisit:

- ★ Adjectival agreement
- ★ *'Avoir' (j'ai - tu as – il/elle a)*
- ★ Describing people's personality

J'ai les cheveux blonds et ondulés. Je porte des lunettes.

J'ai les cheveux noirs et raides. J'ai les yeux verts.

UNIT 3. LES YEUX ET LES CHEVEUX

I can describe what people look like

> De quelle couleur sont tes yeux ? *What colour are your eyes?*
>
> Comment sont tes cheveux ? *What is your hair like?*

J'ai *I have* Je n'ai pas *I don't have* Mon père a *My father has* Ma sœur a *My sister has*	les yeux *eyes* 	bleus *blue* marron *brown* noirs *black* verts *green*	et *and*	je porte *I wear* il/elle porte *he/she wears*	des lunettes *glasses*
				je ne porte pas *I don't wear* il/elle ne porte pas *he/she does not wear*	**de** lunettes
	les cheveux *hair*	blonds *blond* châtains *brown* noirs *black*	frisés *curly* ondulés *wavy* raides *straight*	courts *short* longs *long* mi-longs *medium length*	J'ai *I have* Il/Elle a *He/She has*	des taches de rousseur *freckles* **une barbe** *a beard* **une moustache** *a moustache*
					Je n'ai pas *I don't have* Il/Elle n'a pas *He/She does not have*	**de** taches de rousseur **de** barbe **de** moustache

| Je suis *I am*
Il est *He is* | grand *tall*
petit *short* | mince *slim*
gros *fat* | beau *handsome*
laid *ugly* | brun
roux | brunette
redhead | blond |
| Je suis *I am*
Elle est *She is* | grande
petite | mince
grosse | belle
laide | brune
rousse | | blonde |

THE LANGUAGE GYM

Unit 3. I can describe what people look like: LISTENING

1. Listen and complete with the missing syllable

a. Châ _ _ _ _ _

b. Mar _ _ _

c. Mous _ _ che

d. Rous _ _

e. Fri _ _ _

f. Bru _ _

g. _ _ _ be

h. Lunet _ _ _

i. On _ _ lés

j. _ _ _ de

| ron | lai | sés | bar | tes |
| ne | du | ta | se | tains |

2. Faulty Echo: Underline the mispronounced words

e.g. J'ai les <u>cheveux</u> noirs et longs.

a. Mon père a les cheveux courts.

b. Ma mère a les cheveux blonds.

c. De quelle couleur sont tes yeux?

d. J'ai les yeux bleus.

e. Elle a les yeux marron.

f. J'ai les cheveux mi-longs.

g. Comment sont tes cheveux?

h. Mon père a une barbe.

3. Break the flow: Draw a line between words

a. J'ailesyeuxvertsetjeportedeslunettes.

b. Jen'aipaslesyeuxmarronetjen'aipasdebarbe.

c. Monfrèrealescheveuxlongsetraides.

d. Jen'aipasdemoustache.J'ailescheveuxcourts.

e. Masœurestrousseeetellealescheveuxondulés.

f. Dequellecouleursonttesyeux?Ilssontverts.

g. Commentsonttescheveux?Ilssontchâtains.

h. Masœurn'apasdetachesderousseur.Ellealesyeuxbleus.

4. Listen and tick the correct answer

		1	2	3
a.	J'ai les cheveux	noirs et courts	courts et raides	marron et courts
b.	Mon père a	les yeux noirs	les yeux verts	les yeux marron
c.	Ma grand-mère est	blonde et elle a les cheveux raides	rousse et elle a les cheveux longs	brune et elle a les cheveux frisés
d.	Mon ami Luc	est petit et mince	est grand et mince	est petit et beau
e.	Je suis	grande et laide	belle et petite	grosse et petite

5. Spot the Intruder

Identify and underline the word that the speaker is NOT saying

e.g. J'ai les cheveux noirs, <u>longs</u> courts et raides.

a. Comment sont tes cheveux? J'ai les cheveux noirs, suis frisés et courts.

b. De quelle couleur sont tes yeux? J'ai les yeux noirs bleus.

c. Je suis grande et mince. J'ai les yeux bleus. Je n'ai pas de les taches de rousseur.

d. Ma sœur est petite et belle. Elle a et les cheveux châtains.

e. Mon frère aîné est assez grand mais il est un gros.

f. Mon ami Laurent a les cheveux courts et il a une barbe moustache.

 THE LANGUAGE GYM

6. Listen and tick: True or False? ✓

	True	False
a. My friend Véro is tall.		
b. My uncle Pierre is short.		
c. I have blue eyes.		
d. She has green eyes.		
e. My father wears glasses.		
f. My mother has freckles.		
g. My brother is a redhead.		
h. My sister is a brunette.		
i. I am beautiful and slim.		
j. He has a beard.		
k. I am a redhead and handsome.		

7. Fill in the grid in English

	Eyes	Hair
a. Anne		
b. Marius		
c. Agathe		
d. Jules		
e. Camille		
f. Noé		

8. Narrow Listening. Gapped translation

a. I have _____ eyes and _____ curly_____. I am _____ tall and a little _____. Normally, I am very _____ and I get on well with my _____ Serge. He is short and _____. He has _____ eyes and he wears _____. He is a _____ and he has short and _____ hair.

b. What colour are your _____? I have _____ eyes and _____ _____ hair. I am very _____ and quite _____. I have a black _____, but he is a little _____. In general, I am quite _____ and _____, but I don't _____ with my sister. She is _____ and beautiful. She has _____ eyes and she has _____. She has _____, wavy hair.

9. Catch it, Swap it

Listen, correct the French, then translate the new word/phrase

e.g. Mon frère a les cheveux noirs et ~~frisés~~ raides.

	e.g. straight
a. Mon père est petit et il a une barbe.	a.
b. De quelle couleur sont tes yeux? Ils sont bleus.	b.
c. Je n'ai pas les cheveux longs. Je suis rousse.	c.
d. Je suis assez grand et très mince. J'ai une barbe.	d.
e. Mon ami Julien est un peu gros et très amusant.	e.
f. Ma cousine a onze ans. Elle est petite et brune.	f.
g. Je suis assez actif. J'ai les cheveux blonds et raides.	g.

10. Sentence Bingo

Write 4 of the sentences into the grid. You will hear sentences in French in a RANDOM ORDER. Tick all 4 of your sentences to win bingo.

1. Mon ami Pascal est grand et beau.
2. Ma grand-mère porte des lunettes.
3. J'ai les yeux marron et verts.
4. J'ai les cheveux noirs, courts et frisés.
5. Mon chat est paresseux et beau.
6. Mon père a des taches de rousseur.
7. Je n'ai pas de barbe ni de moustache.
8. Mon chat est assez grand mais un peu gros.
9. Je ne suis pas grande mais je suis mince.
10. Mon grand-père Hector a une barbe.

THE LANGUAGE GYM

11. Listening Slalom

Listen and pick the equivalent English words from each column – drawing a line as you follow the speaker.

e.g. Ma mère a les cheveux noirs, longs et raides. Elle est grande.

My mother has long, straight and black hair. She is tall.

You could colour in the boxes for each sentence in a different colour and read out the sentence in French.

e.g.	**My mother**	but I am tall.	I wear glasses.	I am not tall.
a.	I have	is a redhead.	medium length hair	she is slim.
b.	My friend Isabelle	I have brown	**and black hair.**	He wears glasses.
c.	I am not handsome	**has long, straight**	blond hair, but	and I have dark hair.
d.	I am very beautiful.	doesn't have a	She has freckles and	and I am a bit fat.
e.	My brother	brown eyes and	I have blue eyes	**She is tall.**
f.	I have freckles.	I have wavy	beard.	I am short.

THE LANGUAGE GYM

Unit 3. I can describe what people look like: READING

1. Sylla-Moles

Read and put the syllables in the cells in the correct order

che	et	Mon	châ	pè	tains	rai	les	re	veux	des

a. *My father has straight and brown hair:* M____ p____ a l___ c_____ r_____ e__ c_____.

j'ai	mar	mais	mous	che	pas	ta	ne	yeux	ron	u	Je	n'ai	les

b. *I don't have brown eyes but I have a moustache:* J__ n'___ p____ l___ y_____ m_____ m_____ j'a_____ u____ m_____.

tes	te	ce	grand	Je	Je	des	suis	por	min	lu	et	net

c. *I am tall and slim. I wear glasses:* J___ s_____ g_____ e__ m_____. J__ p_____ d____ l_____.

de	et	les	châ	gran	veux	tains	Ma	courts	sés	fri	sœur	che

d. *My big sister has short, curly and brown hair:* M__ g_____ s_____ a l__ c_____ c_____, f_____ e__ c_____.

beau	ta	j'ai	pe	as	tit	de	ches	Je	et	rous	suis	seur	des	sez

e. *I am quite short, handsome and I have freckles:* J__ s_____ a____ p____, b____ e__ j'__ d__ t_____ d__ r_____.

THE LANGUAGE GYM

2. Read, match and find the French

A. Match these sentences to the pictures above

a. Ma sœur a les cheveux longs et noirs.

b. Mon grand-père a une barbe.

c. Mon amie Véro a des taches de rousseur.

d. Mon chien est un peu gros mais amusant.

e. Mon chat est assez mince et paresseux.

f. Mon père a une moustache. Il est grand.

g. J'ai les cheveux courts et je porte des lunettes.

h. Mon pingouin est assez grand et très intelligent.

i. J'ai de grands yeux verts.

j. Ma mère est grande et rousse.

B. Read the sentences in task A again and find the French for:

a. My cat
b. A little fat
c. Has black hair
d. Is quite slim
e. Has a beard
f. A redhead
g. Has a moustache
h. My mother is tall
i. Short hair
j. Is quite tall
k. My sister
l. Very clever
m. Big green eyes
n. Wear glasses

3. Read the paragraphs and complete the tasks below

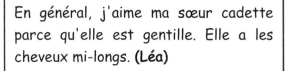

1. J'ai onze ans et j'habite à Toulouse. Je suis gentille et généreuse mais un peu timide. J'ai les cheveux blonds, courts et raides. Je suis assez grande et j'ai les yeux bleus. Je ne porte pas de lunettes. Je m'entends bien avec mon frère aîné parce qu'il est bavard. Il a les cheveux bruns et ondulés et il a une moustache.

En général, j'aime ma sœur cadette parce qu'elle est gentille. Elle a les cheveux mi-longs. **(Léa)**

2. J'habite à Clermont et j'ai treize ans. Je suis assez intelligent et actif. Je suis roux. J'ai les cheveux courts. Je n'ai pas de taches de rousseur. Je ne m'entends pas bien avec ma mère parce qu'elle est sévère. Elle a les yeux marron et les cheveux longs et noirs. Elle a quarante-cinq ans. Je m'entends très bien avec mon grand-père. Il a un chat un peu gros et amusant qui s'appelle Latte. **(Maël)**

A. For each sentence tick one box	True	False
a. **Léa** is generous but very shy.		
b. She has short, straight and blond hair.		
c. She is quite tall and has green eyes.		
d. Her sister has medium length hair.		
e. **Maël** is quite intelligent and active.		
f. He has short and wavy hair.		
g. His mum has blue eyes.		
h. His grandfather's cat is a little fat.		

B. Find the French for:
a. With my older brother
b. I am a redhead
c. I am quite tall
d. I don't wear glasses
e. Because she is strict
f. I like my little sister
g. A bit fat and funny
h. She is 45 years old
i. Mid-length
j. I get on really well with
k. Long and black hair
l. She has brown eyes

C. Read the sentences again and decide if they refer to Léa or Maël

a. ... is 13 years old.
b. Grandfather's cat is called Latte.
c. Gets on well with older brother.
d. Mum is strict.
e. Brother has brown hair.
f. Lives in Clermont.
g. Mother has long black hair.
h. Brother has a moustache.

 **THE LANGUAGE GYM**

4. Tiles Match. Pair them up

6. I am very tall	1. I wear glasses
3. I am a redhead	d. Je porte des lunettes	b. J'ai une barbe	2. Brown eyes	c. Assez petite
5. I have a beard	4. Quite short	f. Les yeux marron	e. Je suis très grande	a. J'ai les cheveux roux

5. Tick or Cross

A. Read the text and tick the box if you find the words in the text, cross it if you do not find them

Je m'appelle Céline. J'ai dix ans et j'habite à Tours. Mon anniversaire est le trois janvier. J'ai deux sœurs et un lapin. Mon lapin est très mince et un peu laid. Je suis active. J'ai les cheveux châtains et frisés. Je m'entends bien avec ma sœur Ellie parce qu'elle est drôle. Elle a les cheveux blonds et ondulés et elle est assez grande. Je m'entends mal avec ma sœur Anne parce qu'elle est antipathique. Elle a les cheveux mi-longs.

		✓	✗
a.	Est assez grande		
b.	Mon anniversaire		
c.	Est un peu timide		
d.	Les cheveux courts		
e.	Medium length hair		
f.	...is very slim		
g.	Blond and curly hair		
h.	I have 3 sisters		
i.	Usually, I am lazy		

B. Find the French in the texts above

a. She has blond and wavy hair. _____

b. ...is very slim and a little ugly. _____

c. I have 2 sisters and a rabbit. _____

d. I have brown and curly hair. _____

e. She has medium length hair. _____

THE LANGUAGE GYM

52

6. Language Detective

★ Comment sont tes cheveux? J'ai les cheveux longs, châtains et ondulés. Je porte des lunettes et je suis assez petite. En général je suis timide mais généreuse. Je m'entends bien avec <u>mon père</u> parce qu'il est patient et gentil. Il a quarante-quatre ans. Il a les yeux marron. Il n'a pas de barbe. **Zoé**

★ De quelle couleur sont tes yeux? J'ai les yeux marron. J'ai une petite chienne blanche qui s'appelle Lily. Elle est assez mince et calme. Son anniversaire est le dix février. Je m'entends bien avec mon père parce qu'il est gentil. Il a les cheveux bruns, courts et raides. Il est assez grand. **Arielle**

★ Comment es-tu? Normalement je suis paresseux. J'habite dans un joli village dans le nord de la France. Je suis roux. J'ai les cheveux longs et frisés. Je porte des lunettes. J'ai un chat marron assez gros mais très actif. **Max**

★ Comment es-tu? En général je suis aimable et très bavard. J'ai quatorze ans et j'habite dans une ville près de la côte. J'ai les yeux bleus. J'ai les cheveux châtains, courts et ondulés. Ma mère est brune et belle. **Benoît**

A. Find someone who...

a. ...wears glasses.

b. ...is shy but generous.

c. ...lives in a city near the coast.

d. ...is a redhead and has long and curly hair.

e. ...has a dark haired dad.

f. ...does not have a beard.

g. ...has a beautiful, brunette mum.

h. ...has a quite slim and quiet dog.

i. ...has blue eyes.

B. Find and underline the French in the text. One box is not mentioned!

My father	He is 44 years old	I am kind and very talkative
The 10th of February	He has dark hair	He has brown eyes
Quite fat	What's your hair like?	annoying and strict
In a pretty village	I have blue eyes	I am 14 years old

THE LANGUAGE GYM

Reorder the sentences in the square to translate the paragraph below. Number them 1 to 15. Then write out the paragraph in French.

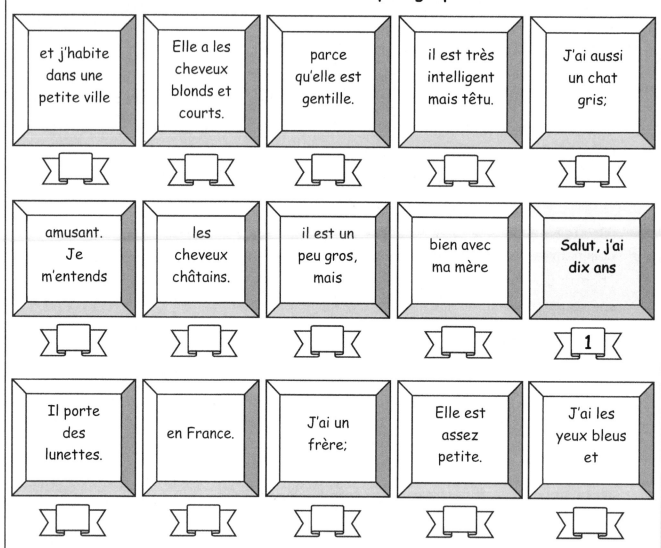

et j'habite dans une petite ville	Elle a les cheveux blonds et courts.	parce qu'elle est gentille.	il est très intelligent mais têtu.	J'ai aussi un chat gris;
amusant. Je m'entends	les cheveux châtains.	il est un peu gros, mais	bien avec ma mère	Salut, j'ai dix ans [1]
Il porte des lunettes.	en France.	J'ai un frère;	Elle est assez petite.	J'ai les yeux bleus et

Hello, I am 10 years old and I live in a small town in France. I have blue eyes and brown hair. I have one brother; he is very intelligent but stubborn. He wears glasses. I also have a grey cat; he is a little fat, but funny. I get on well with my mother because she is kind. She is quite short. She has short blond hair.

8. Crack-it Transl-it

1. Mon chat	2. Comment es-tu?	3. Mon frère	4. les cheveux	5. et
6. les yeux	7. s'appelle Filou.	8. de lunettes.	9. De quelle couleur	10. longs
11. J'ai	12. un peu	13. Je suis assez	14. et raides.	15. Il est
16. châtains	17. a	18. sont tes yeux?	19. ondulés.	20. grand
21. marron.	22. blonds,	23. Je suis rousse	24. gros.	25. il a
26. Je ne porte pas	27. verts.	28. Il est	29. petite	30. noir

C: Crack-it: crack the code and write the sentence in French

T: Transl-it: translate the sentence into English

a. 9-18-11-6-27-23-5-29

C: _____

T: _____

b. 2-13-20-11-4-22-10-5-19-26-8

C: _____

T: _____

c. 1-7-28-30-5-25-6-21-15-12-24

C: _____

T: _____

d: 3-17-6-27-15-20-5-25-4-16-14

C: _____

T: _____

THE LANGUAGE GYM

Unit 3. I can describe what people look like: WRITING

1. Spelling

a. J'__ __ l__ __ y__ __ __ b__ __ __ __.   *I have blue eyes.*

b. M__ sœ__ __ a l__ __ y__ __x v__ __ts.   *My sister has green eyes.*

c. J__ s__ __s b__ __u et r__ __ __ __.   *I am handsome and redhead.*

d. Co__ __ __nt s__ __t t__ __ chev__ __ __?   *What is your hair like?*

e. M__ __ c__ __ __n est u__ p__ __ gr__ __.   *My dog is a little fat.*

f. M__ __ c__ __t e__t t__ __s m__ __ce.   *My cat is very slim.*

2. Anagrams

a. aJ'i esl uexy rtves   *I have green eyes.*

__'__ __ __ __ __ __ __ __ __ __ __ __ __ __ __ __.

b. nMo èper a sel uxehvce strocu   *My father has short hair.*

__ __ __ __ __ __ __ __ __ __ __ __ __ __ __ __ __ __ __ __ __ __ __ __ __ __.

c. eJ en rtope sap ed tutsenle   *I do not wear glasses.*

__ __ __ __ __ __ __ __ __ __ __ __ __ __ __ __ __ __ __ __ __ __ __.

3. Gapped Translation

a. Ma grand-mère est assez petite. Elle a les cheveux blonds, frisés et courts.

My _____ is quite _____. She has _____ _____ and _____ hair.

b. Je suis grand et mince. J'ai les cheveux châtains et raides.

I am _____ and _____. I have _____ and _____ hair.

c. Mon père a une moustache et une barbe. Il est très beau et sympa.

My father has a _____ and a _____. He is very _____ and _____.

THE LANGUAGE GYM

4. No Vowels

a. My grandfather has brown eyes.

M__n gr__nd-p__r__ __ l__s y____x m__rr__n.

b. I wear glasses. I am short and a brunette.

J__ p__rt__ d__s l__n__tt__s. J__ s____s p__t__t__ __t br__n__.

c. My dog is a bit fat but funny.

M__n ch____n __st __n p____ gr__s m____s __m__s__nt.

5. No Consonants

a. My mum is a redhead. She is beautiful.

__a __è__e e____ __ou____e. E____e e____ __e____e.

b. What colour are your eyes?

__e __ue____e __ou__eu__ __o____ __e__ yeu__?

c. My rabbit is slim and it is very small.

__o__ __a__i__ e____ __i____e e__ i__ e____ ____è__ __e__i__.

6. Split Sentences

1. Mon père	a. Elle est un peu petite	1
2. J'ai les cheveux	b. grand	2
3. Je suis assez	c. a pas de barbe	3
4. Ma sœur porte	d. est roux	4
5. Mon grand-père n'	e. châtains et courts	5
6. Comment est ton amie?	f. de rousseur	6
7. J'ai des taches	g. des lunettes	7

THE LANGUAGE GYM

7. Fill in the gaps

a. Comment _____ tes cheveux? J'ai les cheveux_____, longs et _____. Je suis _____ grand et je _____ des lunettes. Je suis assez _____ mais quelquefois assez têtu. J'ai un chat blanc _____ s'appelle Roméo. Il a les yeux _____.

porte	sont	bleus	très	blonds	bavard	qui	frisés

b. Ma sœur s'_____ Annabelle et elle est assez _____. Elle a les yeux _____. Elle a des _____ de rousseur et elle _____ des lunettes. Annabelle a les cheveux noirs, _____ et frisés. Elle a une _____ grise qui est un peu _____ mais très active et joyeuse.

taches	sympa	grosse	courts	appelle	marron	porte	souris

8. Sentence Puzzle

Put the French words in the correct order

a. les J'ai marron yeux suis ne Je grand pas
   I have brown eyes. I am not tall.

b. n' sœur les a blonds Ma pas cheveux est brune Elle
   My sister doesn't have blond hair. She is a brunette.

c. a oncle barbe Mon une Il courts cheveux les noirs et a
   My uncle has a beard. He has black and short hair.

d. Thomas a châtains les ami mi-longs et cheveux Mon
   My friend Thomas has brown and medium length hair.

e. paresseux il chat Mon est mais est très amusant petit beau Il et est
   My cat is very lazy but it is funny. He is handsome and small.

 **THE LANGUAGE GYM**

9. Faulty Translation: write the correct English version

e.g. J'ai les cheveux <u>noirs</u>. ⟹ I have <u>red</u> hair.

e.g. I have black hair.	
a.	
b.	
c.	
d.	
e.	

a. Nadim a une barbe. ⟹ Nadim has a moustache.

b. Mon oncle est gros. ⟹ My uncle has freckles.

c. Je ne suis pas rousse. ⟹ I am not a brunette.

d. Il est grand et mince. ⟹ He is short and slim.

e. Tu es petit et beau? ⟹ Are you tall and handsome?

10. Phrase-level Translation. How would you write it in French?

a. He has blue eyes. _____

b. My sister has long blond hair. _____

c. I have short brown hair. _____

d. What colour are your eyes? _____

e. She is a redhead and she is short. _____

f. I have medium length hair. _____

11. Sentence Jumble: unscramble the sentences

a. les je marron J'ai et des lunettes porte yeux

_____

b. Mon a les et amie porte des Carine frisés cheveux elle lunettes

_____

c. petite assez suis Je suis rousseur je J'ai de et taches belle des

_____

d. frère quatorze ans Mon a cheveux les blonds frisés et Il a

_____

THE LANGUAGE GYM

59

12. Guided Translation

a. C_____ s____ t__ c_____? J'___ l__ c_____ c_____ et l____.
What is your hair like? I have brown and long hair.

b. M__ c_____ a l__ y_____ n_____. I__ e___ u__ p___ g_____.
My dog has black eyes. He is a little fat.

c. M__ c_____ M_____ e____ b_____. E__ e__ p_____ e__ b_____.
My cousin Maude is a brunette. She is short and beautiful.

d. J'__ d_____ a____. J'___ l__ c_____ b_____ e__ f_____.
I am 12 year old. I have blond and curly hair.

13. Tangled Translation

a. Write the French words in English to complete the translation

Hello, **je m'appelle Dylan**. I am 10 years old **et j'habite en Angleterre** with my mother and my father. **J'ai les cheveux châtains** short and curly. **Je suis assez** tall and handsome. I have **bleus** eyes. **Je m'entends bien avec mon père** because he is intelligent **et sympa**. He has brown hair and **il porte des lunettes, mais il n'a pas** beard. **J'ai aussi un chien.** It is a little slim **et très paresseux.**

b. Write the English words in French to complete the translation

I live in Nice, j'ai quatorze ans **and I have two brothers. In general,** je m'entends bien avec mon frère Louis **because he is kind.** Louis est petit **and wears glasses. He has green eyes and** il est roux. **I don't get on well with** mon frère Patrice car il est **a little shy** et têtu. Patrice **has** les cheveux noirs, **long and straight.** He doesn't have de moustache. **Also, I have a white rabbit,** il est un peu gros, **but** il est **funny.**

14. Rock Climbing

Starting from the bottom, pick one chunk from each row to translate the sentences below.

a.	b.	c.	d.	e.
il est très intelligent.	longs et raides.	et elle est gentille.	et j'ai les yeux bleus.	taches de rousseur.
Je suis rousse	Elle a les cheveux courts et frisés	Elle porte des lunettes et elle a des	et les cheveux châtains,	Il est assez mince et
grande et belle.	quatre ans.	J'ai les yeux marron	est brune.	je suis un peu timide.
J'ai treize ans.	En général,	Mon chien a	Ma grand-mère est	Mon amie Aurélie

a. I am 13 years old. I have brown eyes and brown, long and straight hair.

_____

b. In general, I am a little shy. I am a redhead and I have blue eyes.

_____

c. My dog is 4 years old. He is quite slim and he is very intelligent.

_____

d. My grandmother is tall and beautiful. She wears glasses and she has freckles.

_____

e. My friend Aurélie is a brunette. She has short, wavy hair and she is kind.

_____

THE LANGUAGE GYM

15. Staircase Translation

Starting from the top, translate each chunk into French. Write the sentences in the grid below.

a.	I have green eyes	and I wear glasses.				
b.	My father	is quite tall	and has a moustache.			
c.	I get on well	with my sister	because she is kind.	She is a little short.		
d.	I have	black, long hair	and I have brown eyes.	I am very active	but also stubborn.	
e.	What colour	are your eyes?	I have	green eyes.	I am a redhead	and I have freckles.

Answers / Réponses

a.	
b.	
c.	
d.	
e.	

🏆 Challenge / Défi

Can you create 2 more sentences using the words in the staircase grid above?

☆	
☆	

THE LANGUAGE GYM

16. Guided Writing – *Family / Personality / Eyes & Hair*

A. Use the information below to complete the gaps in the French paragraph.

Name: Sarah   Age: 10   City: Grenoble

Personality: kind but lazy   Family: 4 people (mum/dad/sister/me).

Gets on well with grandmother, who is 70

Eyes: blue   Hair: red, long, straight. Freckles.

Extra: black dog called Rémy.

Je m'appelle Sarah. J'ai _____ ans et j'habite à Grenoble. En général je suis _____ mais paresseuse. Dans ma famille _____ quatre personnes: ma mère, mon _____, ma sœur et moi. Je m'_____ bien avec ma grand-mère. Elle ____ soixante-dix ans. J'ai les _____ bleus. Je suis rousse, j'ai les _____ longs et raides. J'ai un _____ noir qui s'_____ Rémy.

B. Now use the information below to write a paragraph in French. Can you add anything else?

Name: Horatio   Age: 11   City: Blois

Personality: active and funny   Family: 4 people (mum/dad/brother/me).

Doesn't get on well with cousin Séverine, who is 15

Eyes: green   Hair: brown, short, wavy. No glasses.

Extra: white cat called Lola

THE LANGUAGE GYM

ORAL PING PONG

UNIT 3 – LES YEUX ET LES CHEVEUX

ENGLISH 1	FRENCH 1	ENGLISH 2	FRENCH 2
I have green eyes.	J'ai les yeux verts.	I have brown eyes.	
I have brown hair.	J'ai les cheveux châtains.	My mother has big blue eyes.	
My father has short hair.	Mon père a les cheveux courts.	I don't wear glasses.	
My sister has blond, long hair.	Ma sœur a les cheveux blonds et longs.	What colour are your eyes?	
He is tall and funny.	Il est grand et amusant.	She is short and a redhead.	
She wears glasses and has freckles.	Elle porte des lunettes et elle a des taches de rousseur.	He has short, curly hair.	
My brother is a redhead and handsome.	Mon frère est roux et beau.	My grandfather has a beard and moustache.	
My dog is a little fat.	Mon chien est un peu gros.	My cat is neither fat nor slim.	

INSTRUCTIONS - You are **PARTNER A.** Work in pairs. Each of you has two sets of sentences - one set has already been translated for you. You will ask your partner to translate these. The other set of sentences have not been translated. Your partner will ask you to translate these.

HOW TO PLAY - Partner A starts by reading out his/her/their first sentence <u>in English</u>. Partner B must translate. Partner A must check the answer and award the following points: **3 points** = perfect, **2 points** = 1 mistake, **1 point** = mistakes but the verb is accurate. If they cannot translate correctly, Partner A will read out the sentence so that Partner B can learn what the correct translation is. Then Partner B reads out his/her/their first sentence, and so on.

OBJECTIVE - Try to win more points than your partner by translating correctly as many sentences as possible.

 THE LANGUAGE GYM

ENGLISH 1	FRENCH 1	ENGLISH 2	FRENCH 2
I have green eyes.		I have brown eyes.	J'ai les yeux marron.
I have brown hair.		My mother has blue eyes.	Ma mère a les yeux bleus.
My father has short hair.		I don't wear glasses.	Je ne porte pas de lunettes.
My sister has blond, long hair.		What colour are your eyes?	De quelle couleur sont tes yeux?
He is neither tall nor short.		She is short and a redhead.	Elle est petite et rousse.
She wears glasses and has freckles.		He has short, curly hair.	Il a les cheveux courts et frisés.
My brother is handsome.		My grandfather has a moustache.	Mon grand-père a une moustache.
My dog is a little fat.		My cat is small and fat.	Mon chat est petit et gros.

INSTRUCTIONS - You are **PARTNER B.** Work in pairs. Each of you has two sets of sentences - one set has already been translated for you. You will ask your partner to translate these. The other set of sentences have not been translated. Your partner will ask you to translate these.

HOW TO PLAY - Partner A starts by reading out his/her/their first sentence <u>in English</u>. Partner B must translate. Partner A must check the answer and award the following points: **3 points** = perfect, **2 points** = 1 mistake, **1 point** = mistakes but the verb is accurate. If they cannot translate correctly, Partner A will read out the sentence so that Partner B can learn what the correct translation is. Then Partner B reads out his/her/their first sentence, and so on.

OBJECTIVE - Try to win more points than your partner by translating correctly as many sentences as possible

 **THE LANGUAGE GYM**

UNIT 4
TU PORTES QUELS VÊTEMENTS?

In this unit you will learn how to say in French:

✓ What clothes you/others wear
✓ Time frames
✓ Verbs – *porter* + clothes / *il fait* + weather

You will revisit:

★ Weather expressions
★ Adjectival agreement

Tu portes quels vêtements à l'école?

À l'école, je porte une chemise blanche, une cravate rouge et un pull gris.

UNIT 4. I can describe what I wear

Tu portes quels vêtements? *What clothes do you wear?*

À l'école *At school* À la maison *At home* Au centre sportif *At the sports centre*	je porte I wear mon ami Pascal porte toujours *my friend* *Pascal* *always* *wears*	une casquette une chemise une cravate une écharpe une jupe une robe une veste	*a cap* *a shirt* *a tie* *a scarf* *a skirt* *a dress* *a jacket*	blanche bleue grise jaune noire orange rose rouge verte violette	*white* *blue* *grey* *yellow* *black* *orange* *pink* *red* *green* *purple*
Quand il fait beau, *When the weather is good,* Quand il fait chaud, *When it is hot,* Quand il fait froid, *When it is cold,* Quand il fait mauvais, *When the weather is bad,*	mon amie Claire porte *my friend* *Claire wears*	un blouson un jean un manteau un pantalon un pull un short un survêtement un t-shirt un uniforme	*a jacket* *jeans* *a coat* *trousers* *a jumper* *shorts* *a tracksuit* *a t-shirt* *a uniform*	blanc bleu gris jaune noir orange rose rouge vert violet	
		des baskets (f) *trainers* des chaussures (f) *shoes*		bon marché *cheap* chers/chères *expensive* confortables gris/grises	
		des collants (m) *tights* des gants (m) *gloves*		marron *brown* noirs/noires verts/vertes	
Je ne porte jamais *I never wear* Mon amie Claire ne porte jamais *My friend Claire never wears*	de*	baskets collants cravate jean			

Author's note:

*When using **ne porte jamais de** you do not use the article (un/une/des) before the noun. You just write **de** instead: **Je ne porte jamais <u>de</u> cravate** – **Mon amie Claire ne porte jamais <u>de</u> baskets**

THE LANGUAGE GYM

Unit 4. What myself and others wear: LISTENING

1. Listen and complete with the missing syllable

a. cas _ _ _ tte

b. cra _ _ te

c. _ _ _ talon

d. chau _ _ _ res

e. _ _ _ _ over

f. _ _ be

g. _ _ _ te

h. é _ _ _ _ pe

i. ju _ _

j. _ _ _ teau

pan	ssu	ves	que	pull
va	man	char	ro	pe

2. Faulty Echo

e.g. *Je porte une cravate* <u>*jaune*</u>.

a. Mon amie Nadia porte un manteau.

b. Je ne porte pas de pull bleu.

c. Mon père porte un jean noir.

d. Des baskets vertes confortables.

e. Un short jaune bon marché.

f. Mon ami Yassine porte une veste.

g. Je porte une casquette violette.

h. Christelle porte une robe rouge.

3. Break the flow: Draw a line between words

a. À la maison je porte une chemise bleue et un pull.

b. À l'école je porte un uniforme vert et bleu.

c. Au centre sportif je porte un short et un t-shirt.

d. À la maison mon frère ne porte jamais de jean.

e. À l'école mon amie Farida porte une jupe violette.

f. Tu portes quels vêtements? Je porte une veste.

g. Au centre sportif je porte des baskets blanches.

THE LANGUAGE GYM

4. Listen and tick the correct answer

		1	2	3
a.	Quand il fait beau, je porte	une casquette blanche	une casquette rose	une casquette noire
b.	Quand il fait mauvais, je porte	un manteau rouge	un manteau bleu	un manteau jaune
c.	Quand il fait chaud,	elle porte une robe	je porte une robe	tu portes une robe
d.	Quand il fait froid,	je porte une écharpe	tu portes une écharpe	il porte une écharpe
e.	Au centre sportif	tu ne portes pas de jupe	je ne porte pas de jupe	elle ne porte pas de jupe

5. Spot the Intruder

Identify and underline the word that the speaker is NOT saying

e.g. Quand il fait mauvais, <u>il y a</u> je porte un manteau.

a. Tu portes quels vêtements? Normalement je porte un jean mais et un t-shirt.

b. Quand il fait chaud, quelquefois je porte un short ou une robe jaune.

c. À l'école, je porte un uniforme. Je porte toujours une chemise grise.

d. Quand il fait mauvais, ma grand-mère porte une écharpe bleue rouge.

e. À la maison ma mère porte des chaussures chères bon marché.

f. Normalement, quand il fait froid je porte un blouson bleu vert et confortable.

g. Mon grand-père ne porte jamais de jean marron et avec de baskets noires.

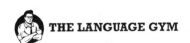
THE LANGUAGE GYM

6. Listen and tick: True or False?

	True	False
a. I always wear a jacket.		
b. My mum wears a pretty skirt.		
c. My brother wears shorts.		
d. I never wear expensive trainers.		
e. My friend wears a dress.		
f. I like my black jumper.		
g. Do you wear a red tie?		
h. My father wears a tie.		
i. Martine wears cheap shoes.		

7. Fill in the grid in English

When it's…	Clothes	Colour
a. good weather		
b.		
c.		white
d.	trousers	
e.		
f.		
g.		yellow
h. hot		
i.	trousers	

8. Narrow Listening. Gapped translation

a. I _____ in Nice. When it is _____, I wear _____ and a red _____.
Also, I wear a _____ at home. I like it a lot because it is _____. I get on
well with my _____ Louis, but he is _____.   Usually,   at   the
_____, Louis wears a blue _____ and _____.

b. I live in the north of _____. When it is _____ weather, I normally wear
_____. However, if it is _____ weather, I normally wear_____
and _____. At school I always wear an elegant _____ shirt, black
_____ and a red _____. I detest _____ a tie, but in my opinion, it is
_____.

9. Catch it, Swap it

Listen, correct the French, then translate the new word/phrase

e.g. À la maison normalement je porte une ~~robe~~ chemise. | e.g. shirt

a. Au centre sportif mon ami porte un jean bleu. | a.

b. Quand il fait chaud, ma mère porte une veste. | b.

c. Quand il fait mauvais, je porte un short. | c.

d. Mon grand-frère porte une chemise jaune. | d.

e. Tu portes quels vêtements ? Je porte un uniforme. | e.

f. Normalement Roland ne porte pas de veste rouge. | f.

g. J'aime ma chemise bleue, mais je n'aime pas ma jupe. | g.

10. Sentence Bingo

Write 4 of the sentences into the grid. You will hear sentences in French in a RANDOM ORDER. Tick all 4 of your sentences to win bingo.

1. Je porte un survêtement blanc très cher.
2. Quand il fait froid, je porte un pull.
3. J'aime mon écharpe car elle est belle.
4. J'aime ma robe, mais elle est chère.
5. À la maison, ma sœur porte un short.
6. Je ne porte jamais de jeans noirs.
7. Mon père porte un blouson gris élégant.
8. À l'école je porte une cravate rose.
9. Tu portes quels vêtements à la maison?
10. Mon ami Sarah porte un uniforme bleu.

THE LANGUAGE GYM

11. Listening Slalom

Listen and pick the equivalent English words from each column

e.g. Quand il fait chaud, je porte un t-shirt blanc et un short.

When it is hot, I wear a white t-shirt and shorts.

You could colour in the boxes for each sentence in a different colour and read out the sentence in French.

e.g.	**When it is hot**	my friend Thérèse	my mother wears	a skirt.
a.	At the sports centre	sometimes	never wears	and a scarf.
b.	At home	my black jacket	**white t-shirt**	comfortable trainers.
c.	When the weather is bad,	a shirt,	a tracksuit and	is hot.
d.	I don't like	**I wear a**	always wears a coat	a green dress.
e.	When it is cold,	my grandfather	but it is	**and shorts.**
f.	I never wear	I normally wear	when it	very elegant.

THE LANGUAGE GYM

Unit 4. I can say what myself and others wear: READING

1. Sylla-Moles

Read and put the syllables in the cells in the correct order

noir	te	Je	bleu	por	et	un	jean

a. *I wear black and blue jeans:* J__ p_____ u___ j_____ n___ et b_____.

te	re	pe	por	u	pè	char	ne	Mon	é

b. *My father wears a scarf:* M____ p_____ p_____ u__ é_____.

Au	ment	cen	sur	te	blanc	tre	por	spor	vê	il	un	tif	te

c. *At the sports centre he wears a white tracksuit:* A__ c_____ s_____ i__ p_____ u__ s_____ b_____.

u	Quand	cas	je	fait	te	por	il	ne	beau	quet	te

d. *When the weather is good, I wear a cap:* Q_____ i__ f_____ b_____, j__ p ___ u___ c_____.

il	re	rou	man	mè	Quand	ma	fait	te	froid	teau	un	ge	por

e. *When it's cold, my mother wears a red coat:* Q_____ i__ f___ f_____, m__ m____ p_____ u__ m_____ r_____.

THE LANGUAGE GYM

2. Read the paragraphs and complete the tasks below

1. Tu portes quels vêtements à l'école? Généralement, je porte une chemise blanche, un pull bleu, une cravate grise et un pantalon noir à l'école. J'ai les cheveux courts, blonds et raides. Je n'ai pas de taches de rousseur et je ne porte pas de lunettes. Je m'entends très bien avec mon ami Frank parce qu'il est très bavard. Il a treize ans. Quand il fait beau, il porte toujours un short, un t-shirt et une casquette. (Éric)

2. J'ai quatorze ans et je suis très active. J'ai les cheveux noirs et je suis assez belle. Au centre sportif, je porte généralement un beau survêtement et des baskets blanches. Quand il fait froid, je porte quelquefois une veste jaune et une écharpe bleue très confortable. Je ne m'entends pas très bien avec mon père. Il a quarante-deux ans et il est strict. Il a une barbe et il porte une chemise et une cravate. (Camille)

A. For each sentence tick one box	True	False
a. Éric wears a white shirt at school.		
b. He wears a green tie.		
c. He has freckles and glasses.		
d. His friend Frank usually wears jeans.		
e. Camille has black hair.		
f. She gets on well with her father.		
g. She wears a red jacket.		
h. Normally she doesn't wear a tracksuit.		
i. Her dad wears a shirt and tie.		

B. Find the French for:

a. When the weather is good
b. A blue scarf
c. Blond, straight hair
d. In the sports centre
e. Grey tie and black trousers
f. I am quite beautiful
g. He has a beard
h. Because he is very talkative
i. He is 13 years old
j. He is strict
k. A blue jumper
l. He always wears

C. Read the sentences again and decide if they refer to Éric or Camille

a. Gets on well with my friend.
b. Sometimes wears a yellow jacket.
c. Father is 42 years old.
d. Has short, blond and straight hair.
e. Normally wears a pretty tracksuit.
f. Wears a t-shirt and cap.
g. Wears black trousers.
h. Has white trainers.

THE LANGUAGE GYM

3. Read, match and find the French

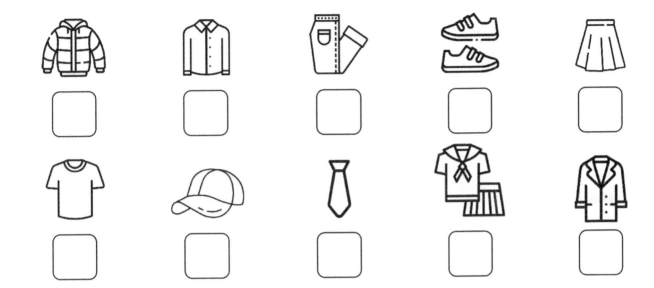

A. Match these sentences to the pictures above

a. Normalement je porte une casquette jaune.

b. J'aime mon uniforme vert car il est confortable.

c. Mon grand-père porte toujours un manteau gris.

d. Quand il fait chaud, je porte un t-shirt bleu.

e. À l'école je porte une cravate rouge.

f. Quand il fait froid, quelquefois, je porte un jean.

g. Ma sœur Émilie porte une jupe noire.

h. J'aime mon manteau parce qu'il est très joli.

i. Au centre sportif, je porte des baskets.

j. À la maison, mon père ne porte pas de chemise.

B. Read the sentences in task A again and find the French for:

a. A grey coat
b. At school I wear
c. It's very pretty
d. I like my coat
e. When it is hot
f. Doesn't wear
g. It is comfortable
h. Wears a black skirt
i. At home my father
j. Always wears
k. I wear jeans
l. I like my uniform
m. A yellow cap

THE LANGUAGE GYM

4. Tiles Match. Pair them up

f. J'aime ma cravate	2. At home

d. Un pull bleu	b. Quand il fait froid	5. She wears jeans	1. Blue jumper	c. Elle porte un jean
3. I like my tie	a. Il porte un t-shirt vert	e. À la maison	4. When it is cold	6. He wears a t-shirt

5. Tick or Cross

A. Read the text. Tick the box if you find the words in the text, cross it if you do not find them.

Je m'appelle Sophie, j'habite à Auch et j'ai quinze ans. En général je suis sympa, mais un peu paresseuse. J'ai les cheveux bruns et longs. À la maison, je porte un t-shirt, mais quand il fait froid, je porte un pull. J'aime mon uniforme parce qu'il est confortable. À l'école, je porte une jupe grise, une chemise blanche, des chaussures noires, mais je ne porte pas de cravate. Je m'entends bien avec mon ami Thomas. Il a seize ans et il est assez actif et sympa. Au centre sportif, il porte un survêtement, mais quand il fait chaud, il porte toujours un short.

		✔	✗
a.	Je suis sympa		
b.	Je n'aime pas ma jupe		
c.	Quand il fait chaud		
d.	Elle porte un pull rose		
e.	Black shoes		
f.	I like my uniform		
g.	Thomas is 17 years old		
h.	He never wears shorts		
i.	Sophie has brown hair		

B. Find the French in the texts above

a. At home, I wear _____

b. He is quite active and nice _____

c. But when it is cold _____

d. Because it is comfortable _____

e. A grey skirt, a white shirt _____

6. Language Detective

★ Tu portes quels vêtements? À la maison, en général je porte un survêtement confortable ou un short. À l'école, je porte une chemise blanche, un pull vert et des chaussures noires. Je n'aime pas mes chaussures, mais elles sont bon marché. Quand il fait froid, je porte un manteau bleu. **Romain**

★ J'ai les cheveux courts et bouclés. À la maison, je porte parfois une jupe jaune ou une robe marron. Je n'aime pas mon uniforme car il n'est pas confortable. **Martine**

★ J'habite dans un village dans le sud de la France avec mon père. En général, mon père porte un t-shirt et une casquette. Quand il fait mauvais, il porte une veste noire et un pantalon gris. **Jérôme**

★ Tu portes quels vêtements quand il fait mauvais? En général je porte des vêtements confortables. J'aime ma robe violette. Je suis un peu petite et je ne porte pas de pantalon ou de jean. Au centre sportif, je porte parfois un survêtement ou un short. **Béa**

A. Find someone who...

a. ...wears grey trousers.

b. ...has short, curly hair.

c. ...doesn't like their shoes.

d. ...has a purple dress.

e. ...wears a brown dress.

f. ...lives in the south of France.

g. ...doesn't like their uniform.

h. ...normally wears comfy clothes.

i. ...wears a black jacket.

j. ...has a dad who wears a cap.

k. ...wears shorts at home.

l. ...wears a tracksuit at the sports centre.

B. Find and underline the French in Romain's text. One box is not mentioned!

In the house	Or shorts	A white shirt
At school	What clothes do you wear?	When it is cold
I don't like	But they are cheap	A green jumper
Comfy tracksuit	But at school	And black shoes
A blue coat	I wear	In general,

77

7. Square This!

Reorder the sentences in the square to translate the paragraph below. Number them 1 to 15.

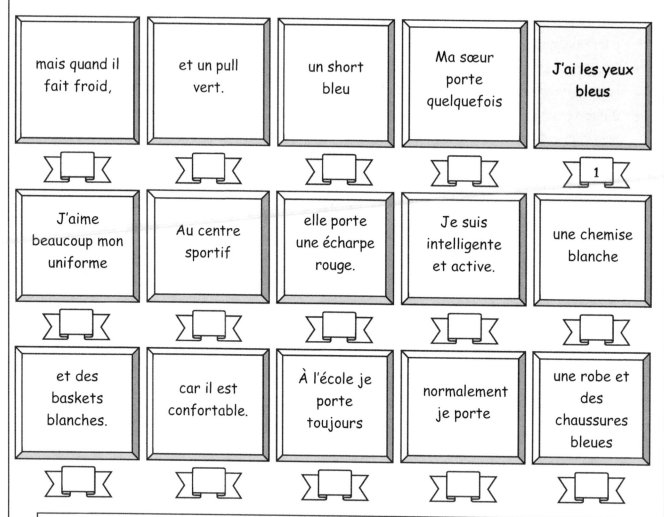

mais quand il fait froid,	et un pull vert.	un short bleu	Ma sœur porte quelquefois	J'ai les yeux bleus
				1
J'aime beaucoup mon uniforme	Au centre sportif	elle porte une écharpe rouge.	Je suis intelligente et active.	une chemise blanche
et des baskets blanches.	car il est confortable.	À l'école je porte toujours	normalement je porte	une robe et des chaussures bleues

I have blue eyes. I am intelligent and active. At the sports centre, I normally wear blue shorts and white trainers. At school I always wear a white shirt and a green jumper. I really like my uniform because it is comfortable. My sister sometimes wears a dress, and blue shoes, but when it is cold, she wears a red scarf.

8. Crack-it Transl-it

1. il est confortable	2. À l'école	3. À la maison	4. Je l'aime	5. elle porte
6. mon amie	7. mon père	8. normalement	9. un uniforme	10. je porte
11. de jupe.	12. Au centre sportif	13. un short	14. quand il fait beau	15. car
16. mais	17. une jupe bleue	18. Ma sœur ne porte pas	19. et une veste rouge.	20. porte
21. Quand il fait froid,	22. et un jean bleu.	23. des baskets	24. un t-shirt	25. et élégant
26. Quand il fait chaud,	27. très beau:	28. un pantalon et	29. car il est confortable	30. un pull

C: Crack-it: crack the code and write the sentence in French

T: Transl-it: translate the sentence into English

a. 3-10-24-22-21-7-20-28-30

C: _____

T: _____

b. 18-11-26-5-13-29

C: _____

T: _____

c. 12-8-6-20-23-16-5-24-14

C: _____

T: _____

d: 2-10-9-27-17-19-4-15-1-25

C: _____

T: _____

THE LANGUAGE GYM

Unit 4. I can say what I and others wear: WRITING

1. Spelling

a. U__ __ é__ __ __ __ __ __ __ __ r__ __ __ __.   *A red scarf*

b. J__ p__ __ __ __ __ u__ j__ __ __ __.   *I wear jeans.*

c. I__ p__ __ __ __ __ u__ p__ __ __ __ __ __ __.   *He wears trousers.*

d. T__ por__ __ __ que__ __ vêt__ __ __ __ __ __?   *What clothes do you wear?*

e. J'__ __ d__ __ cha__ __ __ __ __ __ __ noi__ __ __.   *I have black shoes.*

2. Anagrams

a. À al nsaimo ej repto nu lupl   *At home I wear a jumper.*

__ __ __ __ __ __ __ __ __ __ __ __ __ __ __ __ __ __ __ __.

b. aM œusr torep enu etauceqst eeulb   *My sister wears a blue cap.*

__ __.

c. lI rotep nu naolptna sigr   *He wears grey trousers.*

__ __ __ __ __ __ __ __ __ __ __ __ __ __ __ __ __.

3. Gapped Translation

a. Quand il fait froid, normalement, mon père porte un manteau noir.

When it is _____, normally, my father_____ a black _____.

b. À l'école je porte un uniforme gris. Je ne l'aime pas, mais il est élégant.

At _____ I wear a _____ uniform. I don't like it, but it's _____.

c. Quelquefois, mon amie Farida porte une jupe et une chemise confortable.

_____, my friend Farida wears a _____ and a comfy _____.

4. No Vowels

a. When the weather is good, I wear a cap.

Q__ __nd __l f__ __t b__ __ __ __, j__ p__rt__ __n__ c__sq__ __tt__.

b. I don't wear a purple tracksuit.

J__ n__ p__rt__ p__s d__ s__rv__t__m__nt v__ __ l__t.

c. At home, my mother sometimes wears a dress.

__ l__ m__ __s__n, m__ m__r__ p__rt__ q__ __lq__ __f__ __s __n__ r__b__.

5. No Consonants

a. At school I wear a green tie.

À __ __'é__o__e __e __o__ __e u__e __ __a__a__e __e__ __e.

b. When it's hot, my uncle wears shorts.

__ua__ __ i__ __ai__ __ __au__, __o__ o__ __ __e __o__ __e u__ __ __o__ __.

c. My friend Julie normally wears a scarf.

__o__ a__ie __u__ie __o__ __e __o__ __a__e__e__ __ u__e é__ __a__ __e.

6. Split Sentences

1. Quand il fait	a. porte une jupe
2. À la maison je porte	b. car il est élégant
3. Quelquefois ma sœur	c. un manteau noir
4. J'aime mon uniforme	d. froid, je porte une écharpe
5. Je n'aime pas ma chemise	e. au centre sportif?
6. Mon grand-père porte	f. des vêtements confortables
7. Tu portes quels vêtements	g. car elle est chère

1	
2	
3	
4	
5	
6	
7	

THE LANGUAGE GYM

7. Fill in the gaps

a. Salut, _____ douze ans et j'habite en _____. Je suis assez _____ et je porte des lunettes. À la maison normalement je porte des _____ confortables, un t-shirt_____ ou un _____. Quand il fait froid, je porte ____ pull. Je l'aime beaucoup, mais il n'est pas _____. Et toi? Tu _____ quels vêtements?

un	j'ai	vêtements	survêtement	portes	France	blanc	élégant	grand

b. Tu aimes porter quels vêtements? En _____, je porte un jean _____ et des _____. Je ne _____ pas très actif. À la maison j'aime_____ un_____ et un _____. Je m'entends _____ avec mon frère Marc. À l'école Marc porte une _____ blanche, un pantalon gris et _____ cravate jaune.

baskets	bleu	bien	chemise	général	short	porter	t-shirt	une	suis

8. Sentence Puzzle

Put the French words in the correct order

a. fait un il mauvais, porte pull Quand je
When it's bad weather, I wear a jumper.

b. Tu quels portes vêtements? un porte jupe une jean je noire ou Normalement bleu
What clothes do you wear? Normally I wear a black skirt or blue jeans.

c. amie ne Lou Mon porte pas de blanches baskets
My friend Lou doesn't wear white trainers.

d. est mère grande Ma porte un noir et elle un pantalon rouge pull Quelquefois
My mother is tall. Sometimes she wears black trousers and red jumper.

e. onze ans J'ai général un porte t-shirt je un blanc et short En
I am 11 years old. I usually wear a white t-shirt and shorts.

9. Faulty Translation: write the correct English version

e.g. *Ma jupe est rouge.* ⟹ *My shirt is red.* | e.g. *My skirt is red.*

a. Mon père porte un jean. ⟹ My father wears shorts. | a.

b. Je porte un uniforme élégant. ⟹ I wear a comfy uniform. | b.

c. J'aime mon manteau rose. ⟹ I like my pink shoes. | c.

d. À la maison je porte un pantalon. ⟹ At school I wear trousers. | d.

e. Tu portes quoi à l'école? ⟹ What do you wear at home? | e.

10. Phrase-level Translation. How would you write it in French?

a. I wear trainers. _____

b. I don't wear a red jumper. _____

c. My grandfather wears a blue coat. _____

d. My uniform is comfortable and elegant. _____

e. What do you wear at school? _____

f. I don't like my black shoes. _____

11. Sentence Jumble: unscramble the sentence

a. aime écharpe mon jaune J' est car confortable elle

_____

b. amie Sarah porte un Mon short quelquefois

_____

c. n' ma grise veste bon Je car pas est elle marché aime

_____

d. maison Normalement la je survêtement porte un à orange

_____

THE LANGUAGE GYM

12. Guided Translation

a. T_ p_____ q___ v_____ a__ c_____ _____?
What clothes do you wear at the sports centre?

b. N_____ j__ p____ d__ c_____ b____ e__ u__ p_____ b____.
I normally wear blue shoes and white trousers.

c. M___ p_____ n__ p_____ p___ d__ b_____.
My father doesn't wear trainers.

d. À l__ m_____ q_____ j_ p_____ u__ r_____ j_____.
At home sometimes I wear a yellow dress.

e. Q____ â____ a t___ f_____? I__ a d_____ a___.
How old is your brother? He is two years old.

13. Tangled Translation

a. Write the French words in English to complete the translation.

I am 10 years old. **Je suis assez grand et je suis** active and funny. **Normalement,** at home I wear **des vêtements confortables:** a t-shirt and shorts. À l'école je porte a white shirt, **un pantalon noir et une** red tie. **Je n'aime pas mon uniforme,** but it is comfortable. At the sports centre **je porte un survêtement** blue and green.

b. Write the English words in French to complete the translation.

My friend s'appelle Anne et elle a douze ans. **She has blue eyes** et elle a les cheveux longs et frisés. En général, **she wears a purple dress** et une écharpe rose. **At school** Anne porte un uniforme très élégant: **a grey skirt and a green jumper.** Quand il fait froid, **she wears a coat,** mais ce n'est pas très confortable. Quelquefois, **when the weather is good,** Anne porte **a cap.** À la maison elle porte **cheap clothes.**

14. Rock Climbing

Starting from the bottom, pick one chunk from each row to translate the sentences below.

mon uniforme.	et belle.	chaussures confortables.	pull orange.	t-shirt blanc.
violette et des	et un	je porte un	mais elle est chère	bleu. J'aime
normalement	de manteau	ma veste verte,	porte un short	une casquette
je ne porte jamais	porte toujours	mon ami Karim	je ne porte jamais	à la maison
Quand il fait chaud,	À l'école	Quand il fait mauvais,	Ma cousine Sophie	En général,
a.	b.	c.	d.	e.

a. When it's hot, my friend Karim wears shorts and a white t-shirt.

_____

b. At school I never wear a blue coat. I like my uniform.

_____

c. When the weather is bad, at home normally I wear an orange jumper.

_____

d. My cousin Sophie always wears a purple cap and comfortable shoes.

_____

e. In general, I never wear my green jacket, but it is expensive and pretty.

_____

THE LANGUAGE GYM

15. Staircase Translation

Starting from the top, translate each chunk into French.

Write the sentences in the grid below.

a.	My mum wears	black trousers.				
b.	At the sports centre	I always wear	trainers.			
c.	I don't like	my uniform,	but it is	elegant.		
d.	When it is cold	Manon sometimes	wears a red jacket	and a white	scarf.	
e.	I never wear	shorts	because they are not	comfy.	At home	I wear a tracksuit.

Answers / Réponses

a.	
b.	
c.	
d.	
e.	

🏆 Challenge / Défi

Can you create 2 more sentences using the words in the staircase grid above?

☆	
☆	

THE LANGUAGE GYM

No Snakes No Ladders

7 A pink cap	6 At school I wear a uniform	5 What clothes do you wear?	4 I wear black trousers	3 My friend wears a jacket	2 I wear a green shirt	1 At home I wear a tracksuit DÉPART
8 A red scarf	9 I don't wear a blue tie	10 When it is cold	11 When the weather is bad	12 She wears a grey skirt	13 He wears trainers	14 When it is hot
23 Pretty shoes	22 When the weather is good	21 My friend wears jeans	20 A yellow jumper	19 My mum wears an elegant dress	18 I wear brown shorts	17 A purple shirt
24 A blue tracksuit	25 Black jeans	26 I don't wear shorts	27 At the sports centre I wear	28 Pascal wears a cap	29 Aaron doesn't wear shoes	30 A comfy jacket
					15 I never wear a coat	16 I always wear a t-shirt ARRIVÉE

No Snakes No Ladders

DÉPART	**1** À la maison je porte un survêtement	**2** Je porte une chemise verte	**3** Mon ami(e) porte une veste	**4** Je porte un pantalon noir	**5** Tu portes quels vêtements?
6 À l'école je porte un uniforme	**7** Une casquette rose				
8 Une écharpe rouge	**9** Je ne porte pas de cravate bleue	**10** Quand il fait froid	**11** Quand il fait mauvais	**12** Elle porte une jupe grise	**13** Il porte des baskets
14 Quand il fait chaud	**15** Je ne porte jamais de manteau				
16 Je porte toujours un t-shirt	**17** Une chemise violette	**18** Je porte un short marron	**19** Ma mère porte une robe élégante	**20** Un pull jaune	**21** Mon ami(e) porte un jean
22 Quand il fait beau	**23** Des belles chaussures				
24 Un survêtement bleu	**25** un jean noir	**26** Je ne porte pas de short	**27** Au centre sportif je porte	**28** Pascal porte une casquette	**29** Aaron ne porte pas de chaussures
30 Une veste confortable	**ARRIVÉE**				

THE LANGUAGE GYM

UNIT 5

COMMENT EST TA ROUTINE?

In this unit you will learn how to say in French:

- ✓ What your daily routine is like
- ✓ Time frames/variety of verbs
- ✓ How you get to school

You will revisit:

- ★ Connectives
- ★ Time markers

Comment est ta routine?

En semaine, normalement, je me réveille à sept heures et je vais à l'école.

THE LANGUAGE GYM

UNIT 5. I can describe my daily routine

Comment est ta routine? *What's your daily routine?*

D'abord *First* **D'habitude** *Usually* **En semaine** *During the week* **Le matin** *In the morning* **Normalement** *Normally* **Tous les jours** *Every day*	je me lève — *I get up* je me réveille — *I wake up*		**à six heures** *at six*
	je me brosse les cheveux — *I brush my hair* je me brosse les dents — *I brush my teeth* je me douche — *I have a shower* je me lave — *I wash*		**à sept heures** *at seven* **à huit heures** *at eight*
	je prends le petit déjeuner — *I have breakfast* je me couche — *I go to bed* je me détends — *I relax* je m'habille — *I get dressed* je mets mon uniforme — *I put on my uniform*		**à neuf heures** *at nine* **tôt** — *early* **tard** — *late*
	je vais à l'école *I go to school* je vais au centre sportif *I go to the sports centre*		**à pied** — *walking* **en bus** — *by bus* **en voiture** — *by car* **en train** — *by train*

et ensuite *and then*	**de plus** *moreover*	**cependant** *however*	**mais** *but*

L'après-midi *In the afternoon* **La nuit** *At night* **Le soir** *In the evening*	je déjeune — *I have lunch* je dîne — *I have dinner* je fais les devoirs — *I do homework* je joue avec mes amis — *I play with my friends* je lis un livre — *I read a book* je regarde la télé — *I watch TV* je rentre à la maison — *I return home*	

*Author's note. Be mindful that in French **'me'** can mean 'myself'. It is used in reflexive verbs: verbs where the actions you *do to yourself*. E.g. Je **me** douche = *I shower 'myself'.*

THE LANGUAGE GYM

Unit 5. I can describe my daily routine: LISTENING

1. Listen and complete with the missing syllable

a. je dé_ _ _ ne   f. je me _ _ _ che

b. le ma _ _ _   g. je me _ _ tends

c. je _ _ _ bille   h. je me _ _ _ che

d. en voi_ _ re   i. en _ _ maine

e. les _ _ _ veux   j. je me _ _ veille

dé jeu ré se m'ha
dou tin cou che tu

2. Faulty Echo

e.g. Le matin, je me douche.

a. Je me réveille à six heures.

b. Je me lève et je me lave.

c. Je me douche et je m'habille.

d. Je vais à l'école à huit heures.

e. L'après-midi, je fais les devoirs.

f. Je rentre à la maison et je lis un livre.

g. Le soir, je dîne.

h. Je regarde la télé et je me couche.

3. Break the flow: Draw a line between words

a. L'aprèsmidi,jedéjeuneetjejoueavecmesamis.

b. Lematin,jemeréveilleàsixheures.

c. Ensemaine,jevaisàl'écoleàhuitheures.

d. D'abord,jemelève,jeprendslepetitdéjeuneretensuitejem'habille.

e. Lesoir,jeregardelatéléetjemedétends.

f. Commenttesttaroutine?Jemeréveilleetjemedouche.

g. Jemebrosselesdents,jemebrosselescheveuxetjemetsmonuniforme.

THE LANGUAGE GYM

4. Listen and tick the correct answer

		1	2	3
a.	Le matin	je me réveille à six heures	je me lève à six heures	je me douche à six heures
b.	L'après-midi	je rentre à la maison	je joue avec mes amis	je fais les devoirs
c.	Le soir	je regarde la télé	je me détends	je lis un livre
d.	Je vais à l'école	à pied	en bus	en voiture
e.	Tous les jours	je me brosse les cheveux	je me couche	je me brosse les dents

5. Spot the Intruder

Identify and underline the word or words that the speaker is NOT saying

e.g. Le matin <u>parfois</u> je me douche à huit heures.

a. Comment est ta routine? En semaine je me lève lave à six heures.

b. Le matin, je me réveille à sept heures et je prends le petit déjeuner tard.

c. En semaine, je vais à l'école à pied à neuf heures.

d. L'après-midi, je rentre à la maison d'abord et ensuite je joue avec mes amis.

e. Tous les jours, je me brosse les cheveux et je me brosse les dents à neuf heures.

f. Le soir, je regarde la télé, ensuite je dîne et cependant je lis un livre.

g. Le matin, je me te lève tôt et ensuite je mets mon uniforme.

h. D'abord, je m'habille et ensuite je vais à l'école en voiture à pied.

6. Listen and tick: True or False?

	True	False
a. In the morning I get up at 6.		
b. At night I watch TV.		
c. In the afternoon I relax.		
d. First, I brush my teeth.		
e. Every day I have dinner.		
f. I wake up at 8.		
g. I go to school by train.		
h. I don't go to school by bus.		
i. I go to the sports centre by car.		

7. Fill in the grid in English

When	Routine(s)
a. In the morning	
b.	
c.	Wake up
d. At 7	
e.	
f.	
g.	
h.	Brush teeth
i.	

8. Narrow Listening. Gapped translation.

a. My name is Rose and I _____ in a small _____ in France. I have _____ hair and _____ eyes. In the _____ I_____ at six. I have a shower and I _____. Then I _____ by _____. In the afternoon I _____ and I have dinner at _____ with my family.

b. My name is Jean-Louis _____ I am very _____. I have short, _____ hair and _____ eyes. In the morning I _____ at _____. Moreover, I have breakfast and I _____. Then I put my _____ on and I go to school by _____. In the evening I _____, watch TV and I _____ at ten.

9. Catch it, Swap it

Listen, correct the French, then translate the new word/phrase.

e.g. Le matin, je me ~~lève~~ *réveille* à six heures. | *e.g. wake up*

a. L'après-midi, je rentre à la maison et je lis un livre. | a.

b. Tous les jours, je me douche et ensuite je m'habille. | b.

c. Normalement je vais à l'école en train. | c.

d. Le soir, je vais au centre sportif à pied. | d.

e. Je me réveille à huit heures et je me lave. | e.

f. Le matin, d'abord, je prends le petit déjeuner. | f.

g. En semaine, je me couche tard, à neuf heures. | g.

10. Sentence Bingo

Write 4 of the sentences into the grid. You will hear sentences in French in a RANDOM ORDER. Tick all 4 of your sentences to win bingo.

1. L'après-midi, je me détends.
2. Le soir, je regarde la télé et je lis un livre.
3. L'après-midi, je joue avec mes amis.
4. Tous les jours, je me lève à sept heures.
5. Comment est ta routine?
6. Parfois je vais à l'école en bus.
7. Le matin, je vais au centre sportif à pied.
8. La nuit, je me couche à dix heures.
9. Le matin, je prends le petit déjeuner.
10. En semaine, je me réveille à six heures.

11. Listening Slalom

Listen and pick the equivalent English words from each column.

e.g. En semaine, je me lève à sept heures et je me douche.

During the week I get up at seven and I have a shower.

You could colour in the boxes for each sentence in a different colour and read out the sentence in French.

e.g.	**During the week**	in the afternoon	then I watch TV.	and I have breakfast.
a.	In the morning	I return home	I go to bed	walking.
b.	Every day	first I have dinner	**at seven**	I do my homework.
c.	In the afternoon	**I get up**	I play	at nine.
d.	What's your daily routine?	I brush my teeth	I get dressed	**and I have a shower.**
e.	In the evening	I wake up,	and I go to school	Moreover, I read a book.
f.	In the morning	During the week	early and	with my friends.

THE LANGUAGE GYM

1. Sylla-Moles

Read and put the syllables in the cells in the correct order.

me	veil	res	à	Je	heu	ré	le	sept

a. *I wake up at seven:* J__ m__ r_____ à s____ h_____.

je	mi	mes	vec	L'a	a	di	a	près	joue	mis

b. *In the afternoon I play with my friends:* L'a_____-m_____, j__ j__ a_____ m___ a_____.

je	lè	che	tin	me	et	Le	bros	me	veux	les	ve	se	je	ma

c. *In the morning I get up and I brush my hair:* L__ m_____, j__ m__ l____ et j__ m__ b_____ l__ c_____.

de	la	je	et	Le	lé	je	gar	té	soir	dî	re	ne

d. *In the evening I have dinner and I watch tv:* L__ s___, j__ d_____ et j__ r_____ l__ t____.

à	le	heu	ma	re	l'é	tu	en	tin	Le	à	co	vais	voi	je	huit	res

e. *In the morning I go to school by car at 8:* L__ m_____, j__ v___ à l'é_____ e__ v_____ à h_____ h_____.

THE LANGUAGE GYM

96

2. Read the paragraphs and complete the tasks below

1. Comment est ta routine? En semaine, je me lève tôt, je prends le petit déjeuner, je me brosse les dents et ensuite je vais à l'école à pied à huit heures. A l'école, je porte une chemise blanche, un pantalon gris et une cravate. L'après-midi, parfois, je rentre à la maison à quatre heures. D'abord, je fais les devoirs. De plus, je joue avec mes amis et je regarde la télé. Le soir, normalement, je dîne à sept heures et je me couche à neuf heures. **(Jérôme)**

2. J'habite à Marrakech et j'ai treize ans. J'ai les yeux verts et les cheveux roux. J'ai trois frères et je m'entends bien avec ma mère. Tous les jours, je me réveille à huit heures, je me douche, je me brosse les cheveux et je m'habille. Mais, le samedi, je me lève tard et je vais au centre sportif en bus. D'habitude, l'après-midi, je lis un livre. Le soir, je dîne avec ma famille et ensuite je me détends. Je ne regarde jamais la télé. **(Houda)**

A. For each sentence tick one box	True	False
a. **Jérôme** gets up early during the week.		
b. He goes to school by train.		
c. He wears grey trousers at school.		
d. He returns home at 6pm.		
e. **Houda** has brown eyes.		
f. Every day she has a shower.		
g. On Saturdays she gets up early.		
h. She goes to the sports centre by bus.		
i. She always watches tv.		

B. Find the French for:

a. I have a shower
b. I brush my hair
c. I return home at 4pm
d. First, I do my homework
e. I wear a white shirt
f. I never watch TV
g. I have red hair
h. I wake up at 8am
i. I have 3 brothers
j. But on Saturdays
k. I go to bed at 9pm
l. I brush my teeth
m. I relax

C. Read the sentences again and decide if they describe Jérôme or Houda.

a. Has dinner at 7pm.
b. Gets up early.
c. Reads in the afternoon.
d. Has green eyes and red hair.
e. Walks to school at 8am.
f. Plays with friends.
g. Never watches TV.
h. Has dinner with family.

THE LANGUAGE GYM

3. Read, match and find the French

A. Match these sentences to the pictures above

a. La nuit, parfois, je lis un livre.

b. Tous les jours, je me lave et ensuite je prends le petit déjeuner.

c. En semaine, je vais à l'école à pied à neuf heures.

d. Normalement, le matin, je me lève à sept heures.

e. L'après-midi, je rentre à la maison à six heures et je regarde la télé.

f. Je ne vais jamais au centre sportif en train.

g. Le matin, je me brosse les dents et je me brosse les cheveux.

h. Le soir, d'abord, je dîne et ensuite je me détends.

i. La nuit, je me couche toujours à dix heures.

j. Tous les jours, je joue avec mes amis à l'école.

B. Read the sentences in task A again and find the French for:

a. I go to school

b. I get up at 7am

c. Never

d. I watch TV

e. First I have dinner

f. Walking

g. I brush my hair

h. Every day

i. I always go to bed

j. Then I relax

k. I read a book

l. I have breakfast

m. I play with my friends

4. Tiles Match. Pair them up.

d. Je lis un livre	e. En semaine

4. By car	1. I shower	c. Je m'habille	a. En voiture	f. Je me lève tard
2. I get up late	5. During the week	3. I read a book	b. Je me douche	6. I get dressed

5. Tick or Cross

A. Read the text. Tick the box if you find the words in the text, cross it if you do not find them.

J'habite au Québec. J'ai quinze ans. Je suis gentil mais un peu paresseux. J'ai les yeux marron et les cheveux courts et raides. En semaine, je me lève tard et je ne prends pas le petit déjeuner. Je me brosse les dents, je mets mon uniforme et ensuite je vais à l'école en voiture à neuf heures. À l'école, je porte un pull bleu, un pantalon gris et une cravate. Je déjeune à une heure. L'après-midi, je rentre à la maison à quatre heures. D'abord, je me détends et ensuite je joue avec mes amis. Le soir, je dîne à six heures. Cependant, je regarde la télé. Normalement, je me couche à dix heures.

	✓	✗
a. En semaine		
b. Je déjeune à une heure		
c. Je vais à l'école à pied		
d. Je porte un pull noir		
e. First, I relax		
f. However, I watch TV		
g. Short straight hair		
h. I brush my teeth		
i. I return home at 6pm		

B. Find the French in the texts above

a. At school I wear a blue jumper. _____

b. I have brown eyes. _____

c. Then I play with my friends. _____

d. I go to bed at 10pm. _____

e. I have dinner at 6pm. _____

THE LANGUAGE GYM

6. Language Detective

★ Comment est ta routine? D'habitude, <u>je me réveille</u> à six heures, je me douche et je prends le petit déjeuner. Ensuite, je m'habille et je me brosse les cheveux. En semaine, je vais à l'école en voiture à huit heures. Le soir, je ne dîne pas. Cependant, parfois, je lis un livre la nuit et je me couche à dix heures. **Nadim**

★ J'habite en Belgique et j'ai douze ans. Tous les jours, je me lève à huit heures. D'abord, je prends le petit déjeuner et ensuite je mets mon uniforme. Je porte une jupe noire et un T-shirt rouge. L'après-midi, je joue avec mes amis. Le vendredi, je vais au centre sportif en bus. **Simone**

★ Je suis grand et assez sympa. J'ai vingt ans. J'ai les yeux bleus et j'ai une barbe. Le matin, je me brosse les dents, mais je ne prends pas le petit déjeuner. Je déjeune à midi. De plus, je joue avec mes amis. L'après-midi, je rentre à la maison à six heures et je dîne. **Stéphane**

★ Salut, je m'appelle **Claire** et j'ai quinze ans. Je m'entends très bien avec ma mère parce qu'elle est généreuse. Le matin, je me lève tôt, je m'habille et je vais à l'école à pied. Je déjeune à une heure et je rentre à la maison à quatre heures. Ensuite, je fais les devoirs et je regarde un peu la télé.

A. Find someone who...

a. ...has lunch at 12.
b. ...doesn't have breakfast.
c. ...wears a red t-shirt.
d. ...sometimes reads a book at night.
e. ...wakes up at 6am.
f. ...returns home at 4pm.
g. ...goes to school by car.
h. ...goes to the sports centre by bus.
i. ...gets up early.
j. ...has a generous mum.
k. ...has blue eyes.
l. ...walks to school.
m. ...plays with friends in the afternoon.

B. Find and underline the French in Nadim's text. One box is not mentioned!

~~I wake up~~	I shower	By car
I go to bed	Your daily routine	At night
I get dressed	I read a book	In the morning
At ten	I go to school	However
After	Usually	I brush my hair

Reorder the sentences in the square to translate the paragraph below.
Number them 1 to 15.

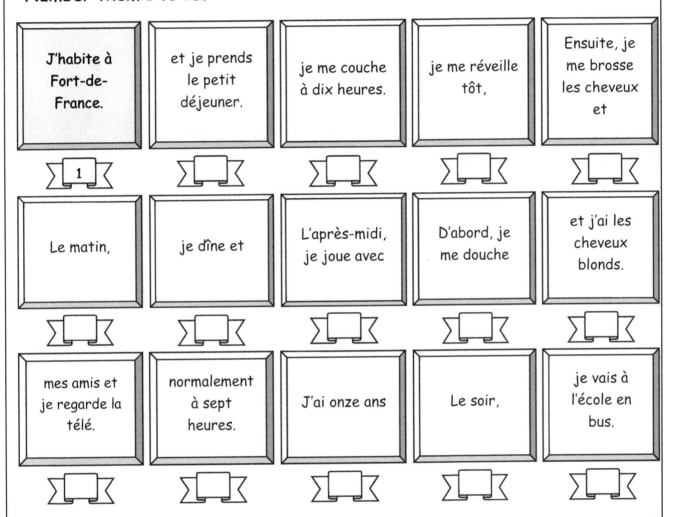

J'habite à Fort-de-France.	et je prends le petit déjeuner.	je me couche à dix heures.	je me réveille tôt,	Ensuite, je me brosse les cheveux et
1				
Le matin,	je dîne et	L'après-midi, je joue avec	D'abord, je me douche	et j'ai les cheveux blonds.
mes amis et je regarde la télé.	normalement à sept heures.	J'ai onze ans	Le soir,	je vais à l'école en bus.

I live in Fort-de-France. I am 11 years old and I have blond hair. In the morning I wake up early, normally at seven. First, I shower and I have breakfast. Then I brush my hair and I go to school by bus. In the afternoon I play with my friends and I watch TV. In the evening I have dinner and I go to bed at ten.

8. Crack-it Transl-it

1. je vais à l'école	2. je rentre à la maison	3. à sept heures	4. l'après-midi	5. tôt
6. je fais les devoirs	7. d'abord je prends le petit déjeuner	8. en semaine	9. parfois	10. à pied.
11. et je me douche	12. je vais au centre sportif	13. je me réveille	14. Le matin	15. et je déjeune
16. je m'habille.	17. à midi.	18. le soir	19. à huit heures	20. ensuite
21. à cinq heures	22. je me lève	23. en bus	24. et je me couche	25. et je dîne
26. je dîne	27. je me détends	28. et je regarde la télé	29. normalement	30. et je lis un livre

C: Crack-it: crack the code and write the sentence in French

T: Transl-it: translate the sentence into English

a. 14-22-3-7-20-16-1-10

C: _____

T: _____

b. 29-13-5-11-19-1-23-15-17

C: _____

T: _____

c. 4-2-21-25-20-6-28

C: _____

T: _____

d: 8-12-10-18-27-30-9-26-3-24

C: _____

T: _____

THE LANGUAGE GYM

Unit 5. I can describe my daily routine: WRITING

1. Spelling

a. L__ m__ __ __ __.   *In the morning.*

b. J__ m__ d__ __ __ __ __.   *I shower.*

c. J__ m__ b__ __ __ __ __ l__ __ d__ __ __ __.   *I brush my teeth.*

d. C__ __ __ __ __ __ __ __ e__ __ __ t__ r__ __ __ __ __ __ __? *What's your daily routine?*

e. J__ d__ __ __ __ __ __ __ à u__ __ __ h__ __ __ __.   *I have lunch at 1pm.*

2. Anagrams

a. eJ am'hblile à spet rheeus   *I get dressed at 7am.*

__ __ __'__ __ __ __ __ __ __ __ __ __ __ __ __ __ __ __ __ __ __.

b. pL'asrè-mdii ej em ddéetns   *In the afternoon I relax.*

__'__ __ __ __ __ __ __-__ __ __ __ __ __ __ __ __ __ __ __ __ __ __.

c. eJ em ccouhe à idx ehurse   *I go to bed at ten.*

__ __.

3. Gapped Translation

a. En semaine, je me lève à sept heures et je me couche tôt.

During the _____ I _____ at seven and I go to _____ early.

b. Tous les jours, je regarde la télé et je lis un livre la nuit.

Every _____ I _____ TV and I _____ a _____ at night.

c. L'après-midi, je rentre à la maison à quatre heures. Ensuite je joue avec mes amis.

In the afternoon I_____home at _____. Then I _____ with my friends.

THE LANGUAGE GYM

4. No Vowels

a. In the morning I wake up late.

L__ m__t__n, j__ m__ r__v__ __ll__ t__rd.

b. First, I relax, then I do homework.

D'__b__rd, j__ m__ d__t__nds, __ns__ __t__ j__ f__ __s l__s d__v__ __rs.

c. At night I go to bed at nine.

L__ n__ __t, j__ m__ c__ __ch__ à n__ __f h__ __r__s.

5. No Consonants

a. During the week I get up at seven.

E__ __e__ai__e, __e __e __è__e à __e__ __ __eu__e__.

b. In the morning I eat breakfast at nine.

__e __a__i__, __e __ __e__ __ __ __e __e__i__ __é__eu__e__ à __eu__ __eu__e__.

c. I brush my teeth every day.

__e __e __ __o__ __e __e__ __e__ __ __ __ou__ __e__ __ou__ __.

6. Split Sentences

1. L'après-midi, je rentre	a. soir, je regarde la télé
2. Chez moi, je porte un T-shirt	b. parce que c'est confortable
3. Le	c. routine?
4. Tous les	d. douche et je m'habille
5. En semaine, je me	e. en voiture
6. Je vais à l'école	f. à la maison
7. Comment est ta	g. jours, je me lève à six heures

1	
2	
3	
4	
5	
6	
7	

7. Fill in the gaps

a. Dans ma _____ il y a cinq personnes. Je m'_____ bien avec ma sœur parce qu'elle est _____. Le matin, je me _____ à sept heures, et ensuite je _____ mon uniforme. Je porte une _____ noire et une veste rouge. Je déjeune à _____ heure. L'après-midi, je regarde la _____ et je me _____ à dix heures.

télé	lève	jupe	couche	famille	une	gentille	entends	mets

b. _____ est ta routine? Le matin, je me réveille à _____ heures, je me douche et je me _____ les dents. _____ je vais à l'école en_____. L'après-midi, je _____ à la maison à quatre _____. _____ je me détends et ensuite je _____ les devoirs. Le soir, je _____ un livre et je dîne avec ma famille.

heures	brosse	rentre	lis	voiture	D'abord	Comment	fais	Ensuite	huit

8. Sentence Puzzle

Put the French words in the correct order

a. le matin, je prends mon uniforme Normalement, je mets le petit déjeuner et
Normally, in the morning, I have breakfast and I put on my uniform.

b. je vais je déjeune à l'école En semaine, à midi en voiture et
During the week I go to school by car and I have lunch at twelve.

c. tôt, Tous les, je réveille me brosse je m'habille et jours les cheveux je me
Every day I wake up early, I get dressed and I brush my hair.

d. douze couche ans à sept heures Je J'ai lève et à dix heures me je me
I am 12 years old. I get up at seven and I go to bed at ten o'clock.

e. à l'école, déjeune je Je avec ma famille dîne mais le soir, à six heures
I have lunch at school, but in the evening I have dinner with my family at six o'clock.

THE LANGUAGE GYM

9. Faulty Translation. Write the correct English version.

e.g. Je me lève à six heures. ⟹ *I wake up at seven.* | **e.g.** *I get up at six.*

a. Le matin, je me douche. ⟹ In the evening I wash. | **a.**

b. Je vais à l'école à pied. ⟹ I go to school by car. | **b.**

c. Je me brosse les dents. ⟹ I brush my hair. | **c.**

d. Je me couche à dix heures. ⟹ I go to bed at nine. | **d.**

e. Je joue avec mes amis. ⟹ I play with my brother. | **e.**

10. Phrase-level Translation. How would you write it in French?

a. I wake up at eight. _____

b. I get dressed and I have breakfast. _____

c. In the afternoon I relax. _____

d. In the morning I brush my teeth. _____

e. During the week I have lunch at twelve. _____

f. I go to the sports centre by bus. _____

11. Sentence Jumble: unscramble the sentences

a. matin, Le heures je à me lève six et prends déjeuner le je petit

_____

b. jours, les Tous brosse me dents je les et brosse cheveux je me les

_____

c. semaine, En je au voiture centre vais sportif en

_____

d. soir, Le regarde je télé la et détends je me

_____

12. Guided Translation

a. C_____ e__ t__ r_____? J__ m__ l____ à s____ h_____.

What's your daily routine? I get up at six o'clock.

b. L__ m_____, j__ n__ p_____ j_____ l__ p_____ d_____.

In the morning I never have breakfast.

c. L'a____-____, j__ j___ a_____ m__ a____ e__ j__ r_____ l__ t____.

In the afternoon I play with my friends and I watch TV.

d. E__ s_____, j__ m'_____ e__ j__ v____ à l'_____ à h____ h_____.

During the week I get dressed and I go to school at eight o'clock.

e. Q_____ â____ a t___ f_____? I__ a d____ a__.

How old is your brother? He is two years old.

13. Tangled Translation

a. Write the French words in English to complete the translation

I live in Paris. **Je m'appelle Marc, j'ai quinze ans et** I am quite tall. **Le matin,** I wake up at seven, **je me lave, je m'habille** and I have breakfast. Then **je me brosse les dents.** I go to school by car **à neuf heures.** I have lunch and **je joue avec mes amis.** In the afternoon I return home **à cinq heures et je me détends.** Sometimes I watch tv.

b. Write the English words in French to complete the translation

J'habite au Havre. Je m'appelle Isabelle et **I am twelve years old.** J'ai un frère, **but I don't have a sister.** Le matin, **I get up at six** et je me douche. **Moreover,** je me brosse les dents **and I brush my hair. I get dressed at seven** et je vais à l'école **walking.** Normalement, je porte un pull vert et **black trousers. I have lunch at one.** L'après-midi, parfois, **I do my homework,** mais je ne regarde jamais la télé. **At night I relax and I go to bed** à dix heures.

THE LANGUAGE GYM

14. Rock Climbing

Starting from the bottom, pick one chunk from each row to translate the sentences below.

je regarde la télé.	à pied.	en voiture.	toujours les dents.	les devoirs.
mais je me brosse	Ensuite,	cheveux mais je ne fais pas	centre sportif	je vais à l'école
je me brosse les	je prends le petit déjeuner,	tôt et	avec ma famille.	ensuite je vais au
d'abord, je me détends,	je dîne	je me douche et	je me réveille	parfois,
En semaine,	L'après-midi,	Le matin,	Tous les jours,	Le soir,
a.	b.	c.	d.	e.

a. During the week I wake up early and I go to school walking.

_____

b. In the afternoon, first I relax, then I go to the sports centre by car.

_____

c. In the morning sometimes I have breakfast, but I always brush my teeth.

_____

d. Every day I have a shower and I brush my hair, but I don't do my homework.

_____

e. In the evening I have dinner with my family. Then I watch TV.

_____

15. Staircase Translation

Starting from the top, translate each chunk into French.

Write the sentences in the grid below.

a.	In the morning	I wake up at eight.				
b.	First	I have breakfast,	and then I get dressed.			
c.	At night	I relax	and I go to bed	at ten.		
d.	Every day	I return home	at four and	I play	with friends.	
e.	During the week	I get up	at seven.	However,	I don't do	my homework.

Answers / Réponses

a.	
b.	
c.	
d.	
e.	

🏆 Challenge / Défi

Can you create 2 more sentences using the words in the staircase grid above?

☆	
☆	

THE LANGUAGE GYM

One pen One dice

Play in pairs. You only have 1 pen and 1 dice.

One person has the pen and starts translating the sentence into **English.** The other person rolls the dice until they roll a 6, they swap the pen and translate. The winner is the person who finishes translating all the sentences first.

1. En semaine, je me lève à sept heures.	
2. Tous les jours, je prends le petit déjeuner et je me brosse les dents.	
3. Le matin, je me douche et je m'habille.	
4. Je me couche à neuf heures et je lis un livre.	
5. Je vais à l'école à pied à huit heures.	
6. L'après-midi, je joue avec mes amis.	
7. Le soir, je dîne. De plus, je regarde la télé.	
8. D'abord, je mets mon uniforme, ensuite je me brosse les cheveux.	
9. Le matin, je me réveille tôt.	
10. L'après-midi, je vais au centre sportif en voiture.	

One pen One dice

Play in pairs. You only have 1 pen and 1 dice.

One person has the pen and starts translating the sentence into **French**. The other person rolls the dice until they roll a 6, they swap the pen and translate. The winner is the person who finishes translating all the sentences first.

1. During the week I get up at 7.	
2. Every day I have breakfast and I brush my teeth.	
3. In the morning I have a shower and I get dressed.	
4. I go to bed at 9 and I read a book.	
5. I go to school walking at 8.	
6. In the afternoon I play with my friends.	
7. In the evening, I have dinner. Moreover, I watch TV.	
8. First I put on my uniform, then I brush my hair.	
9. In the morning I wake up early.	
10. In the afternoon I go to the sports centre by car.	

UNIT 6

TU ÉTUDIES QUELLES MATIÈRES?

In this unit you will learn how to say in French:

- ✓ What school subjects you study
- ✓ Days of the week
- ✓ Opinions - like/dislike

You will revisit:

- ★ Adjectival agreement
- ★ J'aime/Je n'aime pas

Tu étudies quelles matières, Pierre?

J'étudie l'espagnol. J'aime ça parce que c'est utile et amusant.

THE LANGUAGE GYM

112

Unit 6. LES MATIÈRES SCOLAIRES

I can give opinions on school subjects

> **Tu étudies quelles matières?** *What subjects do you study?*

À l'école *At school*	**j'étudie** *I study* **je n'étudie pas** *I don't study*	**l'**	allemand anglais éducation physique espagnol histoire informatique	German English PE Spanish history ICT
Le lundi *On Mondays* **Le mardi** *On Tuesdays* **Le mercredi** *On Wednesdays*	**mon ami(e) étudie** *my friend studies* **mon ami(e) n'étudie pas** *my friend doesn't study*	**la**	biologie chimie géographie religion	biology chemistry geography RE
		le	français	French
		les	arts plastiques sciences/SVT maths	art science maths
Le jeudi *On Thursdays* **Le vendredi** *On Fridays*	**j'ai cours...** *I have a ... lesson* **je n'ai pas cours** *I don't have a ... lesson* **mon ami(e) a cours** *my friend has a ... lesson*	d'allemand d'anglais d'arts plastiques d'espagnol d'histoire	de biologie de français de géographie de maths de sciences	

J'aime *I like*	**l'**	allemand espagnol histoire	**mais** *but*	**c'est** *it is*	amusant barbant compliqué	fun boring complicated
Je n'aime pas *I don't like*	**la**	biologie géographie	**parce que** *because*	**ce n'est pas** *it isn't*	difficile facile fatigant	difficult easy tiring
Mon ami(e) aime *My friend likes*	**le**	français			intéressant relaxant	interesting relaxing
Mon ami(e) n'aime pas *My friend doesn't like*	**les**	sciences maths			utile	useful

THE LANGUAGE GYM

Unit 6. I can give opinions on school subjects: LISTENING

1. Listen and complete with the missing syllable

a. Biolo_ _ _   f. Espa_ _ _ _

b. Informati_ _ _   g. Re_ _gion

c. Géogra_ _ _ _   h. An_ _ _ _ _ _

d. Histoi_ _   i. _ _ _mie

e. Al_ _mand   j. _ _ _ _çais

glais que phie fran gie
li   re   chi   gnol   le

2. Faulty Echo

e.g. J'étudie la <u>musique</u>.

a. J'ai cours d'anglais.

b. J'aime le français.

c. Je n'étudie pas l'informatique.

d. Je n'aime pas la religion.

e. Mon ami a cours d'arts plastiques.

f. Je n'ai pas cours de biologie.

g. Mon amie aime l'allemand.

h. J'aime les maths.

3. Break the flow: Draw a line between words

a. Lemercredi,j'aicoursd'artsplastiques.

b. Levendredi,j'étudiel'espagnoletlagéographie.

c. Lejeudi,jen'aipascoursd'histoireoudesciences.

d. Lemardi,monamiacoursdefrançaisetdereligion.

e. Monamien'aimepasl'anglaismaiselleaimelachimie.

f. Àl'école,j'étudielamusiqueetlabiologie.

4. Listen and tick the correct answer

		1	2	3
a.	J'ai cours d'	allemand	arts plastiques	histoire
b.	Je n'étudie pas	l'anglais	le français	l'informatique
c.	J'étudie l'anglais	parce que c'est amusant	mais c'est barbant	mais c'est compliqué
d.	Je n'aime pas la religion	parce que c'est intéressant	parce que c'est compliqué	parce que c'est amusant
e.	J'aime les sciences	mais c'est compliqué	mais c'est assez difficile	mais c'est assez utile

5. Spot the Intruder

Identify and underline the word that the speaker is NOT saying.

e.g. À l'école __mon ami__ j'étudie la musique et les arts plastiques.

a. Tu étudies quelles matières? J'étudie le français et les sciences maths.

b. Mon amie aime l'italien, mais elle n'aime pas aussi l'espagnol.

c. Le mardi, j'ai cours d'éducation physique et j'aime ça j'adore parce que c'est amusant.

d. Le vendredi, mon ami a cours de chimie, mais utile il n'aime pas ça.

e. Je n'étudie pas l'informatique. Le lundi, j'étudie j'ai cours de biologie.

f. Mon amie étudie les maths. Elle n'aime pas ça mais parce que c'est compliqué.

g. Je n'aime pas la l'histoire parce que c'est compliqué, mais c'est intéressant.

THE LANGUAGE GYM

6. Listen and tick: True or False?

		True	False
a.	On Wednesdays, I have art		
b.	On Tuesdays, I have RE		
c.	I like English because it's interesting		
d.	I don't like history because it's boring		
e.	I like Spanish because it is useful		
f.	I like PE but it is tiring		
g.	Chemistry is difficult		
h.	French is fun		
i.	Geography is easy		

7. Fill in the grid in English

Subject	Opinion
a. German	
b.	
c.	interesting
d.	
e. English	
f.	useful
g. Spanish	
h.	fun
i.	
j.	tiring

8. Narrow Listening. Gapped translation

a. During the week I _____ at seven. First, I have breakfast and I _____ then I go to _____. On _____, I have an _____ lesson. I like it because it is _____. My friend likes _____ because it is _____, but a little _____. And you, what _____ do you study? At school I study _____ and _____.

b. In the morning I wake up at _____. I _____ my teeth and I go to school at _____. I study many _____. I like _____ because it is _____, but I don't like _____ because it is _____. My friend Simone has a _____ lesson on _____. She doesn't like _____, but it is _____.

 **THE LANGUAGE GYM**

9. Catch it, Swap it

Listen, correct the French, then translate the new word/phrase

e.g. Le jeudi, j'ai cours de ~~français~~ **maths**.

		e.g. maths
a.	À l'école, j'étudie les maths et les sciences.	a.
b.	J'aime les arts plastiques parce que c'est fatigant.	b.
c.	Mon ami aime la religion parce que c'est utile.	c.
d.	Le mardi, j'ai cours de chimie et de religion.	d.
e.	Je n'aime pas l'informatique parce que c'est fatigant.	e.
f.	Le vendredi, je n'ai pas cours d'éducation physique.	f.
g.	J'aime beaucoup l'histoire parce que c'est amusant.	g.

10. Sentence Bingo

Write 4 of the sentences into the grid. You will hear sentences in French in a RANDOM ORDER. Tick all 4 of your sentences to win bingo.

1. Mon amie aime le français.
2. Le jeudi, j'ai cours de musique.
3. Le mardi, j'étudie l'anglais et l'espagnol.
4. J'aime les sciences parce que c'est amusant.
5. À l'école j'étudie la biologie.
6. Je n'aime pas les maths, mais c'est utile.
7. Tu étudies quelles matières? J'étudie l'anglais.
8. J'aime la géographie parce que c'est facile.
9. Je n'étudie pas les maths: c'est barbant.
10. J'aime l'informatique parce que c'est facile.

THE LANGUAGE GYM

11. Listening Slalom

Listen and pick the equivalent English words from each column – drawing a line as you follow the speaker

e.g.   *Le lundi j'ai cours de français et de maths.*

   On Mondays I have a French and Maths lesson.

You could colour in the boxes for each sentence in a different colour and read out the sentence in French

e.g.	On Mondays	I have a PE lesson.	I don't like it because	I like it a lot.
a.	My friend likes	I don't study chemistry.	French and	it is very difficult.
b.	On Wednesdays	I have a	I like it a lot	because it is boring.
c.	On Fridays	biology	My friend likes music	maths lesson.
d.	At school	on Tuesdays.	because it is interesting	and useful too.
e.	What subjects do you study?	I study science.	I study geography and	because it is fun.
f.	I don't have a music lesson	I study maths.	I don't like it	but it is tiring.

THE LANGUAGE GYM

Unit 6. I can give opinions on school subjects: READING

1. Sylla-Moles

Read and put the syllables in the cells in the correct order

c'est	glais	l'an	in	que	J'ai	té	ce	res	me	sant	par

a. *I like English because it is interesting:* J'ai_____ l'an_____
p_____ q_____ c'e_____ i_____.

que	la	que	tu	ce	sant	si	J'é	a	die	par	mu	c'est	mu

b. *I study music because it is fun:* J'é_____ l__ m_____
p_____ q____ c'e_____ a_____.

maths	com	J'ai	mais	pli	me	c'est	les	qué

c. *I like maths, but it is complicated:* J'a_____ l_____ m_____,
m_____ c'e_____ c_____.

ai	gie	la	Mon	lo	ti	a	u	bio	mi	le	me	c'est

d. *My friend likes biology, it is useful!:* M___ a_____ a_____ l__
b_____, c'e_____ u_____!

phy	ca	j'ai	si	lun	du	cours	que	Le	d'é	tion	di

e. *On Mondays, I have a PE lesson:* L__ l_____, j'a___ c_____
d'é_____ p_____.

2. Read the paragraphs and complete the tasks below

1. Tous les jours, je me réveille à sept heures, je prends le petit déjeuner et je mets mon uniforme. Ensuite, je vais à l'école en bus à huit heures. D'habitude, à l'école, j'étudie beaucoup de matières. J'aime l'anglais parce que c'est intéressant. J'adore aussi l'éducation physique parce que c'est amusant, mais parfois c'est fatigant. Mon ami aime le français parce que c'est utile. Je n'étudie pas l'histoire parce que c'est barbant. **(Richard)**

2. J'ai onze ans et j'habite au Luxembourg. J'ai les yeux marron et les cheveux longs et frisés. Je suis assez active et sympa. Normalement, je me lève à sept heures et demie, je me douche, je m'habille et je me brosse les dents. Le lundi, j'ai cours de géographie. J'adore ça parce que je m'entends bien avec mon prof. Le mardi, j'étudie le français, les arts plastiques, les maths et les sciences. Je n'aime pas beaucoup les maths parce que c'est compliqué mais utile. **(Sarah)**

A. For each sentence tick one box	True	False
a. Richard wakes up early at six.		
b. He goes to school by bus.		
c. He likes ICT because it's interesting.		
d. He says that history is useful.		
e. Sarah has long straight hair.		
f. She gets up at half past seven.		
g. She gets on well with the geography teacher.		
h. She has French on Thursdays.		
i. She likes maths because it's fun.		

B. Find the French for:

a. Also, I love PE
b. I don't study history
c. On Mondays I have a geography lesson
d. I study many subjects
e. My friend likes French
f. I get on well with my teacher
g. I have brown eyes
h. I go to school by bus
i. But it's sometimes tiring
j. French, art, maths
k. Complicated but useful
l. I brush my teeth
m. On Tuesdays I study

C. Read the sentences again and decide if they refer to Richard or Sarah

a. Gets up at half past seven.
b. Doesn't like maths.
c. Likes English.
d. Is quite active and kind.

e. Has science on Tuesday.
f. Says that PE is fun.
g. Doesn't study history because it's boring.
h. Goes to school by bus at eight.

THE LANGUAGE GYM

3. Read, match and find the French

A. Match these sentences to the pictures above

a. Tous les jours, je vais à l'école en bus.

b. Je n'aime pas l'informatique, mais c'est utile.

c. Le lundi, j'ai cours de géographie à huit heures.

d. J'adore les arts plastiques: c'est relaxant.

e. Mon amie aime l'espagnol parce que c'est utile.

f. Je n'aime pas l'éducation physique: c'est fatigant.

g. Le mercredi, mon ami a cours de biologie.

h. J'étudie la musique parce que c'est amusant.

i. Je n'étudie jamais les maths: c'est compliqué.

j. Je n'aime pas l'anglais parce que c'est barbant.

B. Read the sentences in task A again and find the French for:

a. I love art

b. I never study

c. Tiring

d. But it's useful

e. I study

f. Because it's fun

g. I go to school

h. My friend likes

i. It's complicated

j. I don't like

k. On Wednesdays

l. Because it's boring

m. By bus

 THE LANGUAGE GYM

4. Tiles Match. Pair them up. ✓

c. C'est compliqué	e. Ce n'est pas utile

6. I like chemistry	4. Because it is easy	2. French lesson	1. At school	b. J'aime la chimie

a. Cours de français	f. À l'école	5. It is not useful	3. It's complicated	d. Parce que c'est facile

5. Tick or Cross

A. Read the text. Tick the box if you find the words in the text, cross it if you do not find them.

J'ai quatorze ans et j'habite au Maroc. Je suis gentille, mais parfois bavarde. J'ai les yeux verts et je suis grande. Tous les jours, je me lève à sept heures, je m'habille et ensuite je vais à l'école en bus. À l'école, je porte une jupe bleue et des chaussures noires. Le mardi, j'ai cours d'anglais, de chimie, de français et d'éducation physique. Je n'aime pas la chimie parce que c'est un peu barbant. Je préfère l'éducation physique parce que c'est amusant, mais parfois fatigant. J'adore aussi le français parce que c'est utile et je m'entends bien avec le prof.

	✓	✗
a. Mais parfois bavarde		
b. Je porte une jupe bleue		
c. J'adore aussi le français		
d. Parce que c'est facile		
e. I go to school by car		
f. I prefer maths		
g. I don't like music		
h. A little boring		
i. I have blue eyes		

B. Find the French in the text above

a. I get on well with the teacher _____

b. Every day I get up at 7 _____

c. Fun, but sometimes tiring _____

d. I prefer PE because… _____

e. I have green eyes and I am tall _____

6. Language Detective

★ Tu étudies quelles matières? J'étudie les maths, l'anglais et l'espagnol. Je n'aime pas les maths parce que c'est un peu compliqué. J'adore l'anglais parce que c'est intéressant. J'aime aussi l'espagnol parce que je m'entends bien avec le prof. **Christophe**

★ J'ai treize ans et j'habite en Martinique. Tous les jours, je vais à l'école en train. J'étudie beaucoup de matières. J'adore la géographie parce qu'à mon avis c'est très utile. Je n'aime pas la chimie parce que c'est barbant. Je préfère l'allemand parce que c'est intéressant. **Vanessa**

★ Mon ami s'appelle Marc, il a les cheveux courts et noirs. Il aime l'histoire parce que c'est amusant. Le mardi, il a cours de musique et il aime ça parce que c'est relaxant. Il n'aime pas les sciences parce que c'est barbant. **Théo**

★ Le vendredi j'ai cours d'éducation physique. J'aime beaucoup ça parce que c'est amusant, mais mon ami n'aime pas ça parce que c'est fatigant. Le mercredi, j'étudie la chimie et la religion. Je n'aime pas la chimie parce que c'est compliqué. **Virginie**

A. Find someone who...

a. ...has chemistry on Wednesdays.

b. ...has a friend who likes history.

c. ...gets on well with the teacher.

d. ...prefers German.

e. ...says that chemistry is boring.

f. ...likes PE a lot because it's fun.

g. ...has a friend doing music on Tuesdays.

h. ...doesn't like maths.

i. ...says that geography is very useful.

j. ...studies RE on Wednesdays.

k. ...loves English because it's interesting.

l. ...finds chemistry complicated.

m. ...studies maths, English and Spanish.

B. Find and underline the French in Vanessa's text. One box is not mentioned!

I am 13 years old	I love geography	In my opinion
I live in Martinique	Because it is interesting	Many subjects
I don't study	It's very useful	By train
Chemistry	Every day	I prefer German
Because it is boring	I study	I don't like

THE LANGUAGE GYM

7. Square This!

Reorder the sentences in the square to translate the paragraph below. Number them 1 to 15.

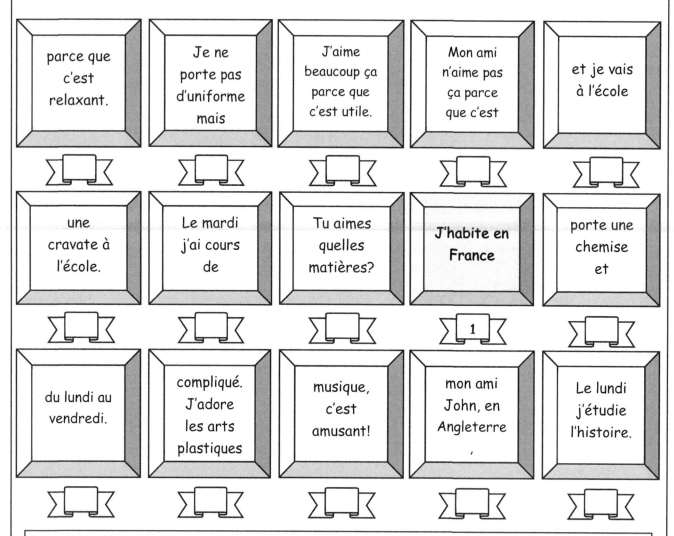

parce que c'est relaxant.	Je ne porte pas d'uniforme mais	J'aime beaucoup ça parce que c'est utile.	Mon ami n'aime pas ça parce que c'est	et je vais à l'école
une cravate à l'école.	Le mardi j'ai cours de	Tu aimes quelles matières?	**J'habite en France** [1]	porte une chemise et
du lundi au vendredi.	compliqué. J'adore les arts plastiques	musique, c'est amusant!	mon ami John, en Angleterre ,	Le lundi j'étudie l'histoire.

I live in France and I go to school from Monday to Friday. I don't wear a uniform, but my friend John, in England, wears a shirt and a tie in school. On Mondays I study history. I really like it because it is useful. On Tuesdays I have a music lesson, it's fun! My friend doesn't like it because it's complicated. I love art because it is relaxing. What subjects do you like?

8. Crack-it Transl-it

1. quelles matières?	2. chimie;	3. À l'école	4. l'informatique	5. l'anglais
6. la géographie	7. amusant	8. je m'entends bien	9. Le jeudi	10. parce que c'est
11. avec mon prof	12. les maths	13. utile	14. barbant	15. mais
16. compliqué	17. j'étudie	18. intéressant	19. je n'aime pas ça	20. et
21. j'adore ça	22. Mon ami	23. j'ai cours de	24. il préfère	25. Tu étudies
26. aime	27. Je n'étudie pas	28. parce que c'est	29. l'espagnol;	30. un peu

C: Crack-it: crack the code and write the sentence in French

T: Transl-it: translate the sentence into English

a. 3-17-29-21-10-13-20-8-11

C: _____

T: _____

b. 9-23-2-19-10-16- 20-30-14

C: _____

T: _____

c. 22-26-4-10-18-15-24-12-28-7

C: _____

T: _____

d: 27-6-15-17-5-10-13-25-1

C: _____

T: _____

THE LANGUAGE GYM

Unit 6. I can say what subject I study: WRITING

1. Spelling

a. J'é__ __die les __ __ths.   *I study maths.*

b. J'étu__ __ __ la géo__ __ __phie.   *I study geography.*

c. J'__ __ cours d'__ __ __ __ plasti__ __ __ __.   *I have an art lesson.*

d. À l'é__ __le, __'__tudie l'__ __pagnol.   *At school, I study Spanish.*

e. J'ai__ __ __ la __ __ __ __mie.   *I like chemistry.*

2. Anagrams

a. À l'Icéoe, j'éuetdi l'glanais te al obiloige   *At school, I study English and biology.*

   __ __'__ __ __ __ __ __, __'__ __ __ __ __ __ __ __'__ __ __ __ __ __ __ __ __ __ __ __ __ __ __ __ __ __ __ __.

b. eL mrecerid, j'ia ocusr ed ciihme   *On Wednesdays, I have a chemistry lesson.*

   __ __ __ __ __ __ __ __ __ __ __, __'__ __ __ __ __ __ __ __ __ __ __ __ __ __ __.

c. noM mai etédui l'ledmalan te el fisnçraa   *My friend studies German and French.*

   __ __ __ __ __ __ __ __ __ __ __ __ __'__ __ __ __ __ __ __ __ __ __ __ __ __ __ __ __ __ __ __ __ __.

3. Gapped Translation

a. À l'école, mon ami étudie les arts plastiques mais il n'étudie pas l'allemand.
    At _____, my _____ studies _____ but he doesn't study _____.

b. Je n'aime pas la chimie parce qu'à mon avis c'est fatigant et compliqué.
    I don't like _____ because in my _____ it is _____ and _____.

c. Après l'école, chez moi, j'étudie le français avec mes frères.
    _____ school, at _____, I study French _____ my _____.

d. J'aime les maths, mais mon ami aime les sciences et la religion.
    I _____ maths, but my _____ likes _____ and _____.

THE LANGUAGE GYM

4. No Vowels

a. After school, I always study maths.

__pr__s l'__c__l__, j'__t__d__ __ t__ __j__ __rs l__s m__ths.

b. At school, I study Spanish and German.

__ l'__c__l__, j'__t__d__ __ l'__sp__gn__l __t l'__ll__m__nd.

c. I like RE because it is interesting.

J'__ __m__ l__ r__l__g__ __n p__rc__ q__ __ c'__st __nt__r__ss__nt.

d. My friend likes science because it is useful.

M__n __m__ __ __m__ l__s sc__ __nc__s p__rc__ q__ __ c'__st __t__l__.

5. No Consonants

a. During the week, at school, I study English.

E__ __e__ai__e, à __'é__o__e, __é__u__ie __'a__ __ __ __ai__.

b. What subjects do you study? I study maths.

__u é__u__ie__ __ue__ __e__ __a__iè__e__? __'é__u__ie __e__ __a__ __ __.

c. On Fridays, my friend has a chemistry lesson.

__e __e__ __ __e__i, __o__ a__i a __ou__ __ __e __ __i__ie.

6. Split Sentences

1. Le lundi	a. les maths
2. Mon ami	b. d'anglais
3. J'aime les sciences:	c. étudie le chinois
4. J'aime	d. chimie
5. Mon amie n'aime	e. j'étudie l'informatique
6. J'ai cours	f. pas l'allemand
7. J'aime la	g. c'est intéressant

1	
2	
3	
4	
5	
6	
7	

THE LANGUAGE GYM

7. Fill in the gaps

a. Salut, j'ai treize _____ et j'habite avec ma _____ à Rouen. Le _____ je vais à l'école. À l' _____ j'étudie l'_____ et les maths. Le _____ j'ai cours d'éducation physique. J'_____ ça parce que c'est amusant. Mon _____ n'aime pas ça parce que c'est _____.

| ami | ans | matin | famille | aime | lundi | fatigant | école | anglais |

b. Tu _____ quelles matières? À l'école j'_____l'_____ mais mon ami _____ l'allemand. J'_____ les arts plastiques parce que c'est _____. Mon _____ n'aime pas les sciences parce que _____ difficile et _____.

| ami | étudies | aime | étudie | espagnol | étudie | intéressant | barbant | c'est |

8. Sentence Puzzle

Put the French words in the correct order

a. j'étudie À les l'école, maths
   At school I study maths.

b. quelles études matières Tu? Le j'étudie lundi et le français l'anglais
   What subjects do you study? On Mondays, I study English and French.

c. l'informatique, mon ami À l'école, le français étudie et l'allemand
   At school, my friend studies ICT, French and German.

d. l'histoire Mon n'aime pas ami, il mais la religion aime
   My friend doesn't like history, but he likes RE.

e. le français et l'allemand j'étudie Le mercredi, l'espagnol étudie mon ami mais
   On Wednesdays, I study German and French, but my friend studies Spanish.

f. parce que les sciences c'est Je n'aime pas compliqué, utile j'étudie la biologie: mais c'est
   I don't like science because it's complicated, but I study biology: it's useful.

THE LANGUAGE GYM

9. Faulty Translation. Write the correct English version.

e.g. *J'étudie le français.* ⟹ *I study <u>German.</u>* | *e.g. I study French.*

a. Le lundi, j'étudie la musique. ⟹ *On Fridays, I study music.* | a.

b. J'étudie l'allemand. ⟹ *I study art.* | b.

c. J'étudie les maths. ⟹ *I study science.* | c.

d. La chimie, c'est fatigant. ⟹ *Chemistry is complicated.* | d.

e. La physique, c'est utile. ⟹ *Physics is tiring.* | e.

10. Phrase-level Translation. How would you write it in French?

a. I study maths and French. _____

b. At school my friend studies German. _____

c. I like art because it is interesting. _____

d. I don't like geography because it is boring. _____

e. What subjects do you study? _____

f. My friend likes Spanish because it is fun. _____

11. Sentence Jumble: unscramble the sentences

a. physique j'étudie À la l'école

_____

b. les maths ami et Mon l'anglais étudie

_____

c. de Le j'ai jeudi français cours

_____

d. religion Mon aime ami la

_____

THE LANGUAGE GYM

12. Guided Translation

a. T__ é_____ q_____ m_____? J'_____ l'_____.

What subjects do you study? I study English.

b. L__ j_____, j__ n'___ p___ c_____ d'i_____.

On Thursdays, I don't have an ICT lesson.

c. L__ m_____, m__ a_____ a c_____ d__ s_____.

On Tuesdays, my friend has a science lesson.

d. L__ m_____ j'_____ l__ f_____ e__ l__ m_____.

In the morning, I study French and maths.

e. À l'_____, m__ a_____ é_____ l'_____ p_____.

At school, my friend studies PE.

13. Tangled Translation

a. Write the French words in English to complete the translation.

I am 13 years old **et j'habite à Avignon** with my family. **En semaine,** normally **je vais à l'école** and I love it. **L'après-midi, je fais** always my homework and **à mon avis** it is important. **À l'école,** on Mondays, **j'étudie les maths** and **l'allemand,** but on Tuesdays, **je n'étudie pas les arts plastiques. Cependant,** my friend **n'étudie pas l'espagnol,** but **il étudie le français.**

b. Write the English words in French to complete the translation.

My name is Gabriel, j'ai quinze ans **and I live** dans une ville **which is called** Bordeaux. Ma mère a les **black hair** et les yeux verts. **I get on well** avec mon père. **In the morning,** le lundi, j'étudie **English,** mais **in my opinion** c'est très **boring.** Cependant, **on Tuesdays,** j'étudie PE **and** je n'aime pas ça parce que **it is very tiring.** Mon ami Paul **doesn't study German,** cependant, **he studies** le français. **He doesn't like** la géographie parce que c'est **complicated.**

14. Rock Climbing

Starting from the bottom, pick one chunk from each row to translate the sentences below.

utile.	compliqué.	difficile.	amusant.	facile.
parce que c'est	parce que c'est	parce que ce n'est pas	parce que ce n'est pas	parce que c'est
Je n'aime pas ça	J'adore ça	Je n'aime pas ça	Elle n'aime pas ça	Il n'aime pas ça
les sciences.	chimie.	informatique.	les maths.	allemand.
je n'ai pas cours d'	j'étudie	mon ami a cours d'	j'ai cours de	mon amie étudie
Le lundi,	Le mardi,	Le mercredi,	Le jeudi,	Le vendredi,
a.	b.	c.	d.	e.

a. On Mondays, I study maths. I don't like it because it is complicated.

_____

b. On Tuesdays, my friend studies science. She doesn't like it because it is not fun.

_____

c. On Wednesdays, I have a chemistry lesson. I love it because it is easy.

_____

d. On Thursdays, I don't have a German lesson. I don't like it because it is not useful.

_____

e. On Fridays, my friend has an ICT lesson. He doesn't like it because it is difficult.

_____

THE LANGUAGE GYM

15. Staircase Translation

Starting from the top, translate each chunk into French.

Write the sentences in the grid below.

a.	On Mondays,	I study maths.				
b.	On Tuesdays,	my friend studies	PE and French.			
c.	On Wednesdays,	I study	ICT	and I like it.		
d.	On Thursdays,	I don't study	English and Spanish.	I don't like them	because they are boring.	
e.	On Fridays,	I always study	history and geography	I love them	and in my opinion	they are relaxing.

Answers / Réponses

a.	
b.	
c.	
d.	
e.	

🏆 Challenge / Défi

Can you create 2 more sentences using the words in the staircase grid above?

☆	
☆	

THE LANGUAGE GYM

132

16. Guided Writing - *Daily routine / school subjects*

A. Use the information below to complete the gaps in the French paragraph.

Name: Anita   Age: 12   Daily Routine: Morning: wakes up at 7, has breakfast, puts on uniform, goes to school at 8.   Afternoon: goes to the sports centre, plays with friends. Evening: dinner, watches TV.

School: On Mondays she has art, biology, Spanish. She likes geography because it is interesting and useful. She doesn't like English because it's boring.

Je m'appelle Anita. J'ai douze _____. Le matin je me _____ à sept heures, ensuite je prends le petit déjeuner, je mets mon uniforme et je _____ à l'école à _____ heures. L'_____ je vais au centre sportif et je joue _____ mes amis. Le soir, je dîne et je _____ la télé. À l'école, le lundi j'étudie les arts plastiques, la biologie et _____. J'aime la géographie parce que c'est _____ et utile. Je n'aime pas l'_____ parce que c'est barbant.

B. Now use the information below to write a paragraph in French. Can you add anything else?

Name: Pierre Age: 13   Daily Routine: Morning: gets up at 7, has breakfast, brushes his teeth, goes to school by bus.   Afternoon: reads a book, plays with friends. Evening: relaxes, goes to bed at 10pm.

School: On Tuesdays he has music and French. He really likes Spanish because it is very useful. He loves PE because it's fun, but it's tiring.

_____

_____

_____

_____

_____

THE LANGUAGE GYM

ENGLISH 1	FRENCH 1	ENGLISH 2	FRENCH 2
I study English and maths.	*J'étudie l'anglais et les maths.*	*At school I study geography.*	
On Tuesdays I have a science lesson.	*Le mardi j'ai cours de sciences.*	*I like PE, but it's tiring.*	
My friend (f) likes German because it's useful.	*Mon amie aime l'allemand parce que c'est utile.*	*On Mondays I have a Spanish lesson.*	
I don't like history because it's boring.	*Je n'aime pas l'histoire parce que c'est barbant.*	*My friend Émilie studies French.*	
On Fridays my friend Dylan has an art lesson.	*Le vendredi mon ami Dylan a cours d'arts plastiques.*	*I like RE because it's interesting.*	
What subjects do you study?	*Tu étudies quelles matières?*	*I don't study maths because it's complicated.*	
I don't study chemistry, I study biology.	*Je n'étudie pas la chimie, j'étudie la biologie.*	*I don't like French, but it's useful.*	
I like ICT because it is interesting.	*J'aime l'informatique parce que c'est intéressant.*	*I like English because it is not boring!*	

INSTRUCTIONS - You are **PARTNER A**. Work in pairs. Each of you has two sets of sentences - one set has already been translated for you. You will ask your partner to translate these. The other set of sentences have not been translated. Your partner will ask you to translate these.

HOW TO PLAY - Partner A starts by reading out his/her/their first sentence <u>in English</u>. Partner B must translate. Partner A must check the answer and award the following points: **3 points** = perfect, **2 points** = 1 mistake, **1 point** = mistakes but the verb is accurate. If they cannot translate correctly, Partner A will read out the sentence so that Partner B can learn what the correct translation is. Then Partner B reads out his/her/their first sentence, and so on.

OBJECTIVE - Try to win more points than your partner by translating correctly as many sentences as possible.

 **THE LANGUAGE GYM**

B

UNIT 6 – LES MATIÈRES SCOLAIRES
ORAL PING PONG

ENGLISH 1	FRENCH 1	ENGLISH 2	FRENCH 2
I study English and maths.		At school I study geography.	À l'école, j'étudie la géographie.
On Tuesdays I have a science lesson.		I like PE, but it's tiring.	J'aime l'éducation physique, mais c'est fatigant.
My friend (f) likes German because it's useful.		On Mondays I have a Spanish lesson.	Le lundi j'ai cours d'espagnol.
I don't like history because it's boring.		My friend Émilie studies French.	Mon amie Émilie étudie le français.
On Fridays my friend Dylan has an art lesson.		I like RE because it's interesting.	J'aime la religion parce que c'est intéressant.
What subjects do you study?		I don't study maths because it's complicated.	Je n'étudie pas les maths parce que c'est compliqué.
I don't study chemistry, I study biology.		I don't like French, but it's useful.	Je n'aime pas le français, mais c'est utile.
I like ICT because it is interesting.		I like English because it is not boring!	J'aime l'anglais parce que ce n'est pas barbant!

INSTRUCTIONS - You are **PARTNER A**. Work in pairs. Each of you has two sets of sentences - one set has already been translated for you. You will ask your partner to translate these. The other set of sentences have not been translated. Your partner will ask you to translate these.

HOW TO PLAY - Partner A starts by reading out his/her/their first sentence <u>in English</u>. Partner B must translate. Partner A must check the answer and award the following points: **3 points** = perfect, **2 points** = 1 mistake, **1 point** = mistakes but the verb is accurate. If they cannot translate correctly, Partner A will read out the sentence so that Partner B can learn what the correct translation is. Then Partner B reads out his/her/their first sentence, and so on.

OBJECTIVE - Try to win more points than your partner by translating correctly as many sentences as possible.

 **THE LANGUAGE GYM**

UNIT 7

MES PROFESSEURS

In this unit you will learn how to say in French:

- ✓ Which teachers you like/don't like
- ✓ Why you like them
- ✓ What makes a good teacher
- ✓ Verbs: *Il/Elle m'aide; Il/Elle m'écoute*

You will revisit:

- ★ School subjects
- ★ Masculine & feminine adjectives

Tu aimes quels professeurs?

J'adore mon professeur de français car il est amusant et il m'aide.

UNIT 7. I can express opinions about my teachers

Tu aimes quels professeurs? *Which teachers do you like?*

J'adore *I love* J'aime beaucoup *I really like* J'aime *I like* Je m'entends bien avec *I get on well with*	mon professeur *my… teacher (male)*	d'anglais d'art dramatique d'éducation physique / d'EPS d'espagnol d'informatique d'histoire de chinois de dessin de français de géographie de maths de musique de sciences	parce qu'il *because he …*	est *is*	bavard — *talkative* divertissant — *entertaining* ennuyeux — *boring* généreux — *generous* gentil — *kind* marrant — *funny* est méchant — *mean* est paresseux — *lazy* est têtu — *stubborn*
			vu qu'il/elle *seeing as he/she…*	est *is*	*drôle — *funny* optimiste — *optimistic* pénible — *annoying* sévère — *strict* sympathique — *nice*
Je n'aime pas *I don't like* Je n'aime pas du tout *I don't like at all* Je ne m'entends pas bien avec *I do not get on well with*	ma professeure *my… teacher (female)*				m'aide — *helps me* m'écoute — *listens to me* me comprend — *understands me* me crie dessus — *shouts at me* ne m'aide pas — *doesn't help me*
			car elle *because she …* mais quelquefois, elle *but sometimes she…*	est *is*	bavarde divertissante ennuyeuse généreuse gentille marrante méchante paresseuse têtue

Author's note:

*The adjectives in this section: "drôle", "optimiste" etc, don't change their endings (unlike gentil/le or méchant/e) so you can use them in both the masculine and feminine forms.

THE LANGUAGE GYM

Unit 7. I can give opinions about teachers: LISTENING

1. Listen and complete with the missing syllable

a. Intelli _ _ _ te   g. Il m'é _ _ _ te

b. Op _ _ miste   h. me com _ _ _ _ _

c. Pa _ _ _ _ te   i. Tê _ _ _

d. M' _ _ tends   j. Pé _ _ ble

e. _ _ resseux   k. Sé _ _ re

f. Mar _ _ _ _   l. Elle m'ai _ _

en	rant	tien	de	gen	cou
ni	tue	prend	pa	vè	ti

2. Faulty Echo

e.g. Mon professeur de <u>chinois.</u>

a. Parce qu'il est gentil.

b. Mon professeur m'écoute.

c. Ma professeure me crie dessus.

d. Mon professeur est drôle.

e. Ma professeure est marrante.

f. Mon professeur m'aide toujours.

g. Ma professeure est ennuyeuse.

h. Mon professeur me comprend.

3. Break the flow: Draw a line between words

a. Maprofesseured'artsplastiquesesttrèsamusante.

b. Jem'entendsbienavecmonprofesseurdemusiquecarilestpatient.

c. J'aimemaprofesseured'anglaisvuqu'elleestsympathiqueetgentille.

d. Jen'aimepasmonprofesseurd'artdramatiquevuqu'ilestasseztêtu.

e. Jenem'entendspasbienavecmaprofesseuredemathscarelleestsévère.

f. Tuaimesquelsprofesseurs?J'adoremonprofesseurdechinois.

g. J'aimemaprofesseuredegéographie,maisquelquefoisellenem'aidepas.

h. J'aimebeaucoupmonprofesseurdefrançaisparcequ'ilestsympathique.

4. Listen and tick the correct answer

		1	2	3
a.	Mon professeur	m'aide	m'écoute	me comprend
b.	Ma professeure	est divertissant	est divertissante	est différente
c.	Ma professeure	est pénible	est patiente	est sympathique
d.	Mon professeur	est paresseux	est patient	est pénible
e.	Ma professeure	de chinois	m'aide	me crie dessus
f.	Mon professeur	est sévère	est sympathique	suis sévère

5. Spot the Intruder

Identify and underline the word that the speaker is NOT saying

e.g. Mon professeur de chinois <u>ne</u> m'aide.

a. Tu aimes beaucoup quels professeurs? Ma professeure de chimie.

b. Ma professeure de les maths est très sympathique.

c. Je n'aime pas mon professeur de biologie parce qu'il est il têtu.

d. J'aime beaucoup elle la professeure de sciences.

e. J'adore ma professeure de la géographie parce qu'elle est marrante.

f. J'adore la ma professeure d'histoire.

g. J'adore ma professeure de dessin parce qu'elle me m'aide comprend.

h. Je m'entends bien avec mon professeur d'espagnol vu qu'il est m'aide.

 **THE LANGUAGE GYM**

6. Listen and tick: True or False?

	True	False
a. My teacher is optimistic.		
b. My teacher is patient.		
c. My teacher is funny.		
d. My teacher is boring.		
e. My art teacher.		
f. My French teacher.		
g. My teacher understands me.		
h. I don't like my teacher.		
i. I don't get on well with my teacher.		
j. My teacher listens to me.		

7. Fill in the grid in English

e.g. My teacher	*is nice*
a. My teacher	
b. I really like	
c.	my teacher
d. My teacher	
e. My teacher	
f. My teacher	
g.	my teacher
h.	the art teacher
i. My teacher	
j.	my French teacher

8. Narrow Listening. Gapped translation

a. Hello, my name is Lorène carver. I _____ in Paris and I _____ like it. I go to _____ every day. On Monday I have maths and _____. I love the _____ teacher because he is _____ and he never shouts at me. However, ___ _____ _____ the chemistry teacher because _____ she is strict and she doesn't _____ ___.

b. ___ _____ is Joanna Drouet and I live in the_____of _____, in Nice. I like it a lot because it is not_____. During the _____ I go to school. On Tuesday I have physics and _____. I like my _____teacher because she is intelligent and she _____ ___, but I don't like ___ _____ the French teacher since she is _____ and impatient.

THE LANGUAGE GYM

9. Catch it, Swap it

Listen, correct the French, then translate the new word/phrase

e.g. Mon professeur de dessin est ~~patient~~ drôle.

	e.g. funny
a. Ma professeure de physique est drôle.	a.
b. Mon professeur de chimie est sympathique.	b.
c. Ma professeure d'allemand est têtue.	c.
d. Je m'entends bien avec mon professeur de maths.	d.
e. J'aime beaucoup ma professeure d'espagnol.	e.
f. Je n'aime pas du tout la géographie car c'est ennuyeux.	f.
g. J'aime mon professeur de chinois vu qu'il est intelligent.	g.

10. Sentence Bingo

Write 4 of the sentences into the grid. You will hear sentences in French.
Tick all 4 of your sentences to win bingo.

1. Mon professeur de sciences est gentil.
2. Ma professeure de dessin est patiente.
3. J'aime beaucoup mon professeur d'histoire.
4. Mon professeur de maths est amusant.
5. Ma professeure de français m'aide.
6. Je n'aime pas mon professeur de musique.
7. Ma professeure de maths me comprend.
8. J'adore mon professeur de chinois.
9. Je n'aime pas l'éducation physique.
10. Ma professeure d'histoire me crie dessus.

THE LANGUAGE GYM

11. Listening Slalom

Listen and pick the equivalent English words from each column – drawing a line as you follow the speaker

e.g. J'aime le dessin car c'est amusant.

    I like art because it is fun.

You could colour in the boxes for each sentence in a different colour and read out the sentence in French

e.g.	I like	my history teacher	but sometimes	listens to me.
a.	I get on well with	is fun	**because**	she is patient.
b.	I don't like at all	**art**	because sometimes	she shouts at me.
c.	I really like	my drama teacher	and sometimes	**it is fun.**
d.	I don't get on with	my maths teacher	since	he is strict.
e.	My Chinese teacher	my Spanish teacher	and also	entertaining.
f.	My English teacher	is patient	because he always	understands me.
g.	My art teacher	is very intelligent	seeing as she never	quite funny.

THE LANGUAGE GYM

Unit 7. I can give opinions about my teachers: READING

1. Sylla-Moles

Read and put the syllables in the cells in the correct order

de	il	re	est	seur	ces	J'a	pro	gen	do	car	mon	scien	fes	til

a. *I love my science teacher because he is kind:* J'a_____ m_____
p_____ d____ s_____ c____ i___ e____ g_____.

seure	m'é	pro	de	d'an	et	Ma	te	glais	fes	cou	m'ai

b. *My English teacher helps me and listens to me:* M____ p_____
d'_____ m'_____ e____ m'_____.

Mon	jours	mu	des	seur	me	pro	si	sus	crie	fes	que	de	tou

c. *My music teacher always shouts at me:* M____ p_____ d___
m_____ m____ c_____ t_____ d_____.

com	chi	me	seure	Ma	nois	prend	pro	ne	fes	de	pas

d. *My Chinese teacher doesn't understand me:* M____ p_____
d____ c_____ n____ m____ c_____ p___.

mar	des	fes	til	Mon	rant	seur	et	sin	pro	gen	de	est

e. *My art teacher is kind and funny:* M____ p_____ d___
d_____ e___ g_____ e___ m_____.

THE LANGUAGE GYM

2. Read the paragraphs and complete the tasks below

1. J'ai treize ans et j'étudie dans une école dans le centre-ville. J'aime beaucoup le chinois parce que c'est intéressant, mais c'est un peu compliqué. Je m'entends bien avec ma professeure de chinois car elle m'aide et elle m'écoute. Le vendredi j'ai cours de biologie, j'adore ça parce que c'est utile et le professeur est marrant. J'adore mon professeur de dessin vu qu'il ne me crie pas dessus et il n'est pas sévère. **(Charlotte)**

2. J'ai dix ans et je vais à l'école primaire à Paris. Le lundi j'ai cours d'anglais à neuf heures, j'adore ça car mon professeur est marrant et il me comprend. À onze heures, j'ai cours d'éducation physique. Je ne m'entends pas bien avec le prof, parce qu'il est méchant et têtu. Le jeudi j'étudie la musique et les sciences. J'adore les sciences parce que c'est intéressant et le professeur est gentil. **(Xavier)**

A. For each sentence tick one box	True	False
a. **Charlotte** really likes Chinese.		
b. Her school is in the city centre.		
c. She loves art because it's useful.		
d. Her art teacher shouts and is strict.		
e. **Xavier** has English on Mondays at 10.		
f. He loves English because his teacher is funny.		
g. His PE teacher is optimistic and kind.		
h. On Thursdays he studies music and science.		
i. His science teacher is lazy.		

B. Find the French for:

a. I really like Chinese
b. She helps me
c. I love my art teacher
d. I love it because it's useful
e. And he is not strict
f. At 11 I have a PE lesson
g. The teacher is kind
h. He doesn't shout at me
i. But it's a little complicated
j. I have an English lesson at 9
k. And understands me
l. I get on well with
m. Mean and stubborn

C. Read the sentences again and decide if they refer to Charlotte or Xavier

a. Has biology on Friday.
b. Gets on well with the Chinese teacher.
c. Loves science.
d. Teacher is stubborn.
e. Goes to a primary school.
f. Doesn't get on well with the PE teacher.
g. Says that biology is useful.
h. Teacher helps and listens to them.

3. Read, match and find the French

A. Match these sentences to the pictures above

a. J'adore ma professeure de musique car elle est optimiste.

b. Je n'aime pas du tout mon professeur d'informatique parce qu'il est sévère.

c. Ma professeure de chinois m'aide toujours.

d. Mon professeur de maths ne me crie pas dessus.

e. Ma professeure d'art dramatique est très marrante.

f. Mon professeur de sciences me comprend.

g. Mon professeur d'éducation physique est patient.

h. J'adore la géographie car le prof m'écoute.

i. Je ne m'entends pas bien avec mon prof d'histoire car il est pénible et paresseux.

j. J'aime ma prof de dessin car elle est intelligente.

B. Read the sentences in task A again and find the French for:

a. My maths teacher
b. ...is very funny
c. Listens to me
d. Always helps me
e. Is annoying and lazy
f. Is intelligent
g. I don't get on with my history teacher
h. My drama teacher
i. I love geography
j. ...because he is strict
k. Understands me
l. Is optimistic
m. Doesn't shout at me

THE LANGUAGE GYM

4. Tiles Match. Pair them up

1. Is mean	b. Mon prof de musique
3. Is stubborn	
2. Is lazy	
d. Est gentil et patient	
f. Est paresseux	
a. Est têtu	
e. Est méchant	
5. My music teacher	
c. M'écoute	
6. Is kind and patient	
4. Listens to me	

5. Tick or Cross

A. Read the text and tick the box if you find the words in the text, cross it if you do not find them

D'habitude je suis assez gentil et travailleur. Tous les jours je vais à l'école en voiture à huit heures et demie. J'adore mon prof d'art dramatique, car il est divertissant, mais parfois il me crie dessus. Le jeudi j'ai cours d'espagnol. Je m'entends bien avec la prof car elle m'aide et elle m'écoute. Je n'aime pas beaucoup mon prof de sciences vu qu'il est un peu sévère et impatient. Aussi, j'aime beaucoup mon prof de français, car il est intelligent et il me comprend. Je ne m'entends pas bien avec ma prof de maths. Elle ne m'écoute jamais! Et toi, tu aimes quels professeurs?

	✔	✗
a. Car il est divertissant		
b. J'ai cours d'anglais		
c. J'adore mon prof		
d. Et il me comprend		
e. My French teacher		
f. I go to school by car		
g. I am quite talkative		
h. Since she helps me		
i. My teacher is kind		

B. Find the French in the texts above
a. What teachers do you like? _____

b. But sometimes he shouts at me. _____

c. On Thursdays I have a Spanish lesson. _____

d. I don't get on with my maths teacher. _____

e. Is a little strict and impatient. _____

6. Language Detective

★ Tu aimes quels professeurs? Je m'entends bien avec mon prof d'éducation physique, parce qu'il est marrant et il m'aide. <u>J'aime aussi</u> ma prof de français car elle est patiente. À mon avis, ma prof d'anglais est gentille et elle ne me crie jamais dessus. **<u>Amélie</u>**

★ Je m'entends bien avec mon prof de sciences, vu qu'il est intelligent et sympa. J'ai cours de chimie le jeudi et le vendredi. Je n'aime pas beaucoup ma prof d'informatique car elle me crie toujours dessus. Je préfère mon prof de chinois parce qu'il est marrant. **<u>Joseph</u>**

★ Mon ami aime l'histoire car c'est intéressant, mais il n'aime pas beaucoup le prof car il est sévère. Il a cours d'arts plastiques le mercredi et il adore ça parce que c'est utile. Il ne s'entend pas bien avec le prof de géographie parce qu'il est pénible et têtu. **<u>Valérie</u>**

★ À l'école j'étudie la musique et l'art dramatique. Je m'entends bien avec le professeur d'art dramatique car il m'écoute et il n'est jamais paresseux. Je ne m'entends pas bien avec mon professeur de maths car il est impatient, un peu méchant et il ne me comprend pas. **<u>Léo</u>**

A. Find someone who...

a. ...doesn't like their maths teacher.

b. ...prefers their Chinese teacher.

c. ...finds the geography teacher annoying.

d. ...finds the French teacher patient.

e. ...has art on Wednesday.

f. ...has an ICT teacher who always shouts.

g. ...says that the history teacher is strict.

h. ...has a science teacher who is clever.

i. ...says the English teacher is kind.

j. ...studies music and drama.

k. ...has a friend who likes history.

l. ...says that the PE teacher is funny.

m. ...loves art because it's useful.

B. Find and underline the French in the text. One box is not mentioned!

I like also	Helps me	Do you like?
Is stubborn	The drama teacher	Is impatient
Chemistry lesson	My science teacher	Always shouts at me
Is kind	Doesn't understand me	At school
Is never lazy	Because he is strict	He doesn't like a lot

7. Square This!

Reorder the sentences in the square to translate the paragraph below. Number them 1 to 15.

Je ne m'entends pas bien avec mon prof de	c'est amusant et le professeur	sévère et elle m'écoute.	jamais dessus. Ma matière	À l'école, j'étudie **[1]**
mais c'est fatigant.	utile et le professeur ne me crie	J'adore l'art dramatique car	me comprend. J'aime	préférée c'est l'éducation physique,
beaucoup de matières fantastiques.	sciences parce qu'il est un peu	J'aime la prof car elle n'est pas	pénible, mais il est gentil.	aussi l'anglais parce que c'est

<u>At school I study</u> many fantastic subjects. I love drama, because it is fun and the teacher understands me. I also like English because it is useful and the teacher never shouts at me. My favourite subject is physical education, but it is tiring. I like the teacher because she is not strict and she listens to me. I don't get on well with my science teacher because he is a little annoying, but he is kind.

THE LANGUAGE GYM

148

8. Crack-it Transl-it

1. il est pénible,	2. marrant,	3. mon professeur de	4. mais	5. dessin
6. optimiste	7. sévère.	8. Je m'entends bien avec	9. parfois	10. espagnol
11. Je n'aime pas	12. ma professeure d'	13. il est impatient	14. elle m'écoute	15. musique
16. elle est patiente	17. il m'aide	18. elle ne me crie jamais dessus	19. elle est sympathique	20. parce qu'
21. j'adore	22. j'aime	23. il ne me comprend pas	24. maths	25. et
26. Aussi	27. beaucoup	28. il est divertissant	29. De plus	30. car

C: Crack-it: crack the code and write the sentence in French

T: Transl-it: translate the sentence into English

a. 8-3-15-30-28-25-2-4-9-23

C: _____

T: _____

b. 22-27-12-10-30-19-25-14

C: _____

T: _____

c. 11-3-5-30-13-25-7-29-1-4-9-17

C: _____

T: _____

d: 21-12-24-20-16-25-6-26-18

C: _____

T: _____

THE LANGUAGE GYM

Unit 7. I can give opinions about my teachers: WRITING

1. Spelling

a. J'__ __ __ __ m__ __ p__ __ __ __ __ __ __ __ __ __r.   *I like my teacher.*

b. M__ __ p__ __ __ __ __ __ __ __ __ __r d__ sci__ __ __ __ __.   *My science teacher.*

c. I__ e__ __ t__ __ __ __ m__ __ __ __ __ __ __.   *He is very funny.*

d. El__ __ __ n__ m__ c__ __ __ __ jam__ __ __ __ des__ __ __ __.   *She never shouts at me.*

e. I__ m'__ __ __ __ __ __ __ __ t__ __ __ __ __ __ __ __ __.   *He always listens to me.*

2. Anagrams

a. eJ n' eiam sap onm epusoserfr ed shiocni   *I don't like my Chinese teacher.*

__ __ ' __.

b. onM epusoserfr ed hiqepusy ste hiyatsqupme.   *My physics teacher is nice.*

__ __.

c. aL eepusoserfr d'iglnasa ste stèr enaetpit.   *The English teacher is very patient.*

__ __ __ __ __ __ __ __ __ __ __ ' __ __ __ __ __ __ __ __ __ __ __ __ __ __ __ __ __ __.

3. Gapped Translation

a. Ma professeure d'allemand me comprend et ne me crie jamais dessus.

My _____ teacher _____ ___ and never _____ at me.

b. J'aime le professeur de dessin car il est amusant et il m'aide.

I_____ my _____ teacher, because he is _____ and he _____ me.

c. J'aime beaucoup la professeure d'anglais vu qu'elle est optimiste et elle m'écoute.

I_____ like my English teacher _____ she is _____ and she _____ to me.

d. Je n'aime pas du tout mon professeur d'art dramatique, car il est quelquefois têtu.

I don't like ___ _____ my _____ teacher, because _____ he is _____.

THE LANGUAGE GYM

4. No Vowels

a. I like my English teacher because he is kind.

J'__ __m__ m__n pr__f__ss__ __r d'__ngl__ __s, c__r __l __st g__nt__l.

b. I don't like my PE teacher: she is stubborn.

J__ n'__m__ p__s m__ pr__f__ss__ __r__ d'EPS: __ll__ __st t__t__ __.

c. I like history, because it is interesting.

J'__ __m__ l'h__st__ __r__, p__rc__ q__ __ c'__st __nt__r__ss__nt.

d. I like my French teacher because he helps me.

J'__ __m__ m__n pr__f__ss__ __r d__ fr__nç__ __s c__r __l m'__ __d__.

5. No Consonants

a. I don't like my science teacher (f).

__e __'ai__e __a__ __a __ __o__e__ __ __ eu__ e __e __ __ie__ __e__.

b. Which teachers do you like?

__u ai__e__ __ue__ __ __ __o__ e__ __ eu__ __?

c. I like my music teacher (m).

__'ai__e __o__ __ __o__e__ __ __ eu__ __e __u__i__ue.

6. Split Sentences

1.	Je m'entends	a. maths est sympathique		1	
2.	La professeure	b la professeure d'anglais		2	
3.	La professeure m'	c. aide		3	
4.	J'aime mon	d. méchante		4	
5.	Le professeur de chinois est	e. est bavarde		5	
6.	Le professeur de	f. professeur de dessin		6	
7.	La professeure est	g. très sévère		7	
8.	Je n'aime pas	h. bien avec mon professeur		8	

THE LANGUAGE GYM

7. Fill in the gaps

a. Salut, j'ai douze _____ et j'aime _____ mon école. J'aime _____ la professeure de _____ ____ elle m' _____ toujours mais je n'aime pas du tout le _____ de maths parce qu'il est _____ et quelquefois il me _____dessus.

| impatient | ans | car | beaucoup | physique | bien | professeur | écoute | crie |

b. Tu _____ quels professeurs? J'_____ beaucoup le professeur ____ chinois car il m'aide _____ et il me _____. De plus, j'aime _____ mon professeur de _____ car il est drôle et optimiste, mais _____il est impatient et il ___ m´écoute pas.

| ne | quelquefois | toujours | aime | musique | aimes | comprend | beaucoup | de |

8. Sentence Puzzle

Put the French words in the correct order

a. Ma d'espagnol professeure très marrante est
   My Spanish teacher is very funny.

b. aimes Tu professeurs quels? aime de maths mon J' professeur
   Which teachers do you like? I like my maths teacher.

c. n' est têtu mon Je parce pas impatient qu'il aime professeur de physique et
   I don't like my physics teacher because he is stubborn and impatient.

d. professeure est gentille elle ma de qu' géographie elle vu et m'aide qu' J'adore
   I love my geography teacher since she is kind and she helps me.

e. professeur qu'il méchant n' mon de aime du français parce pas tout Je pénible et est
   I don't like at all my French teacher because he is annoying and mean.

f. mon de musique est J' aime vu professeur il marrant qu'
   I like my music teacher since he is funny.

9. Faulty Translation: write the correct English version

e.g. My German teacher. ⟹ *Le professeur de <u>dessin</u>.* | *e.g. My art teacher.*

a. My teacher is lazy. ⟹ Mon professeur est têtu. | a.

b. My teacher shouts at me. ⟹ Mon professeur m'écoute. | b.

c. My teacher is optimistic. ⟹ Mon professeur est bavard. | c.

d. My teacher is nice. ⟹ Mon professeur est marrant. | d.

e. My teacher is fun. ⟹ Mon professeur est patient. | e.

10. Phrase-level Translation. How would you write it in French?

a. I like my French teacher. _____

b. I don't like my Spanish teacher. _____

c. I love my music teacher since she is patient. _____

d. I really like my drama teacher because he helps me, but sometimes he is annoying.

_____

e. Which teachers do you like? _____

11. Sentence Jumble: unscramble the sentence

a. aime professeur J' mon d'espagnol

_____

b. aime n' tout professeure Je du ma de musique pas

_____

c. car d' ma est J' anglais intelligente aime professeure elle

_____

d. il mon est pénible professeur aime de sciences, quelquefois J' mais

_____

e. aime m' elle professeure aide et est J' gentille qu'elle ma de chinois parce

_____

THE LANGUAGE GYM

12. Guided Translation

a. T__ a____ q_ p_____? L__ p_____ d'a_____.
Which teachers do you like? The English teacher.

b. J'_____ m___ p_____ d__ m_____ v__ q__i__ e___ g_____.
I like my music teacher since he is kind.

c. M___ p_____ d__ p_____ e__ o_____ et i_____.
My physics teacher is optimistic and intelligent.

d. J'_____ m__ p_____ d__ f_____ c___ i__ n___m__ c__ p___ d_____.
I love my French teacher because he doesn't shout at me.

e. J__ n'____ p__ d_ t____ m__ p_____ d__ c_____. I__ e__ m_____.
I don't like at all my Chinese teacher. He is mean.

13. Tangled Translation

a. Write the French words in English to complete the translation

À l'école, le mardi I study l'anglais, ICT, Spanish and le français. J'aime beaucoup l'anglais because my teacher **est amusante et** understands me. **Aussi,** I like my French teacher **vu qu'il est gentil et il m'aide.** I don't like at all **mon professeur d'informatique car il** is stubborn and strict **mais quelquefois** he helps me. I love my **professeur de français car il** is patient.

b. Write the English words in French to complete the translation

Le matin **I get up** à sept heures et je vais à l'école **at eight.** Tous les jours j'étudie **art, Spanish and science.** Je n'aime pas beaucoup le dessin parce que le professeur **is impatient and a little mean.** J'aime beaucoup mon **Spanish teacher** car **he listens to me** et il est amusant. **I also love** ma professeure de sciences parce qu' **she understands me** et **she is funny.**

14. Rock Climbing

Starting from the bottom, pick one chunk from each row to translate the sentences below.

toujours.	sympathique.	têtu.	ennuyeuse.	il me crie dessus.
mais quelquefois elle est	et	et aussi	et quelquefois	et il m'aide
optimiste	marrante	patient	sévère	impatient
parce qu'il n'est pas	vu qu'elle n'est pas	car il est	vu qu'elle est toujours	vu qu'il est
ma professeure de sciences	mon professeur d'anglais	la professeure d'allemand	mon professeur de maths	le professeur de chimie
J'aime	Je n'aime pas	Je n'aime pas du tout	J'adore	J'aime beaucoup
a.	b.	c.	d.	e.

a. I like the German teacher since she is always funny and also nice.

_____

b. I don't like the chemistry teacher because he is impatient and sometimes stubborn.

_____

c. I don't like at all my English teacher because he is not patient and he shouts at me.

_____

d. I love my science teacher since she is not strict but sometimes she is boring.

_____

e. I really like my maths teacher since he is optimistic and always helps me.

_____

THE LANGUAGE GYM

15. Staircase Translation

Starting from the top, translate each chunk into French.

Write the sentences in the grid below.

a.	My teacher	is kind.				
b.	I really like	my Spanish teacher	because he is not boring.			
c.	I don't like at all	my music teacher	since he is mean	and boring.		
d.	I love	my maths teacher	since she is not annoying,	but sometimes	she shouts at me.	
e.	I like	my English teacher	because he is intelligent	and also optimistic,	but sometimes	he is talkative.

Answers / Réponses

a.	
b.	
c.	
d.	
e.	

🏆 Challenge / Défi

Can you create 2 more sentences using the words in the staircase grid above?

☆	
☆	

THE LANGUAGE GYM

16. Guided Writing - *Myself, clothes, school subjects & teachers*

A. Use the information below to complete the gaps in the French paragraph.

Name: Florence   Age: 12   Lives: Belgium   Personality: patient and kind

Clothes: At home she normally wears a blue t-shirt, at school no uniform

School subjects: Loves science (interesting) and PE (fun but tiring)

Teachers: She likes English teacher (she helps her)

Je m'appelle Florence. J'ai _____ ans et j'habite en Belgique. En général je suis _____ et _____. À la maison normalement je porte un _____ bleu. À l'école je ne _____ pas d'uniforme. J'adore les sciences car c'est _____ et l'éducation physique car c'est _____ mais fatigant. J' _____ bien ma professeure d'anglais car elle m' _____.

B. Now use the information below to write a paragraph in French. Can you add anything else?

Name: Rémi   Age: 13   Lives: Suisse   Personality: shy but funny

Clothes: At home wears shorts and a black t-shirt, at school uniform (likes it)

School subjects: He has history on Monday (but it is boring). He loves maths (useful, but a little complicated)

Teachers: He likes Spanish teacher (she is kind and understands him) but doesn't really like her art teacher (he is strict and doesn't listen to him)

THE LANGUAGE GYM

One pen One dice

Play in pairs. You only have 1 pen and 1 dice.

One person has the pen and starts translating the sentence into **English**. The other person rolls the dice until they roll a 6, they swap the pen and translate. The winner is the person who finishes translating all the sentences first.

1. J'adore mon professeur de dessin parce qu'il est amusant.	
2. J'aime ma professeure de français parce qu'elle est sympathique.	
3. Tu aimes quels professeurs?	
4. Je n'aime pas mon professeur de musique car il est impatient.	
5. J'aime beaucoup mon professeur d'anglais vu qu'il m'écoute.	
6. Je n'aime pas ma professeure de sciences car elle est paresseuse.	
7. Mon professeur d'art dramatique m'aide et il est marrant.	
8. Ma professeure de maths me comprend et elle est patiente.	
9. J'aime bien ma professeure de chinois, mais quelquefois elle est pénible.	
10. Je n'aime pas mon professeur d'histoire car il me crie dessus.	

 THE LANGUAGE GYM

One pen One dice

Play in pairs. You only have 1 pen and 1 dice.

One person has the pen and starts translating the sentence into **French.** The other person rolls the dice until they roll a 6, they swap the pen and translate. The winner is the person who finishes translating all the sentences first.

1. I love my art teacher because he is fun.	
2. I like my French teacher because she is nice.	
3. Which teachers do you like?	
4. I don't like my music teacher because he is impatient.	
5. I really like my English teacher since he listens to me.	
6. I don't like my science teacher because she is lazy.	
7. My drama teacher helps me and he is funny.	
8. My maths teacher understands me, and she is patient.	
9. I like my Chinese teacher but sometimes she is annoying.	
10. I don't like my history teacher because he shouts at me.	

THE LANGUAGE GYM

Printed in Great Britain
by Amazon

23486820R00097